MW00358977

Globe Fearon

Mastering Spelling

Level
D

GLOBE FEARON
Pearson Learning Group

REVIEWERS

Phyllis Aliberto
Port Chester-Rye Union Free School District
Port Chester, New York

Karen L. Bennett
Madera High School
Madera, California

Cassandra E. Meltin, M.A.T., J.D.
Coordinator, Region 3 Chicago Public Schools
Chicago, Illinois

Sally Parker, M.A.
Elk Grove Unified School District
Elk Grove, California

Project Editor: Eleanor Ripp
Production Editor: Regina McAloney
Interior Design: Chris Callaway
Cover Design: Chris Callaway
Electronic Page Production: Linda Bierniak, Debbie Childers, Leslie Greenberg, Mimi Raihl
Photo Researcher: Martin Levick
Editorial Assistants: Jennifer Pereira, Ayanna Taylor, Gina Dalessio
Production Assistant: Pat Gilbanks

Photo Credits: **p.5:** Michael Newman, Photo Edit; **p. 9:** Spencer Grant, Photo Edit;
p. 13: Lawrence Migdale; **p. 17:** Gabe Palmer, The Stock Market; **p. 21:** Frank Siteman, Stock Boston; **p. 25:** Jose Pelaez, The Stock Market; **p. 29:** Steve Skjold, Photo Edit;
p. 33: Bob Daemmrich, Stock Boston; **p. 37:** Chuck Savage, The Stock Market;
p. 41: David Young-Wolff, Photo Edit; **p. 45:** Daniel Schaefer, Photo Edit; **p. 49:** Tony Freeman, Photo Edit; **p. 53:** David Young-Wolff, Photo Edit; **p. 57:** Jeff Greenberg, Photo Edit;
p. 61: Tony Freeman, Photo Edit; **p. 65:** David Young-Wolff, Photo Edit; **p. 69:** David Young-Wolff, Photo Edit; **p. 73:** Dale O'Dell, The Stock Market; **p. 77:** Tony Freeman, Photo Edit;
p. 81: Gregory Scott, Picture Cube; **p. 85:** David Young-Wolff, Photo Edit; **p. 89:** Jon Feingersh, The Stock Market; **p. 93:** David Young-Wolff, Photo Edit; **p. 97:** Bill Bachmann, Photo Edit;
p. 101: Tom McCarthy, Photo Edit; **p. 105:** Tony Freeman, Photo Edit

Copyright © 2000 by Pearson Education, Inc., publishing as Globe Fearon®, an imprint of Pearson Learning Group, 299 Jefferson Road, Parsippany, NJ 07054. All rights reserved. No part of this book may be reproduced or transmitted in any form or by any means, electronic, or mechanical, including photocopying, recording, or by any information storage and retrieval system, without permission in writing from the publisher. For information regarding permission(s), write to Rights and Permissions Department.

ISBN 0-835-94868-4
Printed in the United States of America

6 7 8 9   06 05 04 03

1-800-321-3106
www.pearsonlearning.com

Contents

Words With *ie* and *ei*

Study Words

achieve
seized
briefly
diesel
receiver
skied
convenience
apiece
foreigner
deceive
retriever
protein
relieve
weird
conceited

Additional Study Words

_____

_____

_____

_____

Spelling Rule

Many words in English are spelled with the letters *ie* or *ei*. The rule "*i* before *e* except after *c*" will help you spell most of these words, but for some *ie* or *ei* words, you need to memorize the correct spelling or check in a dictionary.

Example:	*i* **before** *e*	**Except after** *c*	**Just memorize**
	relieve	receiver	weird
	apiece	conceited	seized

A. Say the Words

Say each study word and notice whether it is spelled with *ie* or *ei*. Think about whether it follows the rule "*i* before *e* except after *c*." Then answer the questions below.

B. Write the Words

1. Which eight study words are spelled with *ie*? Write them. Circle *ie* in each word.

_____   _____

_____   _____

_____   _____

_____   _____

2. Which three study words are spelled with *ei* after *c*? Write them. Circle *ei* in each word.

_____   _____

_____

3. Which four study words don't follow the rule? Write them. Circle *ei* in each word.

_____   _____

_____   _____

C. Add Study Words

Think of other words that are spelled with *ie* and *ei*. Write these words below the study words list on this page. You might find new words in advertisements, letters, and newspapers.

Spelling and Language

A. Rhyming Words

Rhyming words have the same ending sounds. Write one or more study words that rhyme with each word below.

Example: brief   leaf

1. weasel _____

2. chiefly _____

3 retreated _____

4. pleased _____

5. beard _____

6. niece _____

7. freed _____

8. beaver _____

_____

9. believe _____

_____

B. Phonetic Spelling

The phonetic spelling of a word is part of a dictionary entry. It shows how a word is pronounced. Read the phonetic spelling of each study word below. Write the correct spelling for each one. For extra help, use the Pronunciation Key on page 107.

Example: (kēp) = keep

10. (ə chēv´)

11. (fôr´ in ər)

12. (ri sēv´ ər)

13. (kən vēn´ yəns)

14. (ri lēv´)

15. (skēd)

16. (ri trēv´ ər)

17. (ə pēs´)

18. (prō´ tēn)

19. (dē sēv´)

20. (sēzd)

21. (dē´ zəl)

22. (wird)

10. _____

11. _____

12. _____

13. _____

14. _____

15. _____

16. _____

17. _____

18. _____

19. _____

20. _____

21. _____

22. _____

Did You Know?

The *diesel* engine is named after its inventor, Rudolph Diesel. The first working model of this engine was displayed in 1898. More than a hundred years later, *diesel* engines still provide the power for much of industry and transportation, all over the world!

Study Words

achieve
seized
briefly
diesel
receiver
skied
convenience
apiece
foreigner
deceive
retriever
protein
relieve
weird
conceited

Build Vocabulary

Read each clue below. Then write the study word that matches it.

1. someone from another country
2. strange or mysterious
3. type of oil-burning engine
4. grabbed or captured
5. part of a telephone
6. slid downhill on two runners
7. to mislead
8. to lessen burden or pain
9. for each person
10. meat and cheese contain this
11. to reach a goal
12. for a short period of time
13. something that makes life easier
14. vain and egotistical
15. a hunting dog

1. _____
2. _____
3. _____
4. _____
5. _____
6. _____
7. _____
8. _____
9. _____
10. _____
11. _____
12. _____
13. _____
14. _____
15. _____

Real-Life Spelling

Reading a Manual

A manual is a document that describes how to use a product or a service. Many things you buy come with manuals that give useful information about getting started with a product. Read these opening paragraphs from a manual for training a new puppy. Find five misspelled study words and write them correctly on the lines.

16. _____

17. _____

18. _____

19. _____

20. _____

Your New Golden Meadows Puppy

Congratulations! You are now the proud owner of a golden retriever puppy from Golden Meadows. We don't want to sound concieted, but we think we raise the most beautiful, lovable puppies in the world. This manual breifly explains the steps involved in training your new puppy. For your pleasure and conveneince, it's important to start training your puppy right away. Remember, training begins with love! For the first few weeks, spend as much time as possible playing with the puppy. Once you have gained your animal's trust, the two of you can move on to acheive a great working relationship.

Spelling Review

Fill in each set of boxes below with a study word. First notice the location of *ie* or *ei* in the word and then count the number of other letters. Write the study words in the puzzle. Each word fits in only one place. The first one has been done for you.

1. | R | E | L | I | E | V | E |

2. | | | I | E | | |

3. | | | I | E | | |

4. | | | | | | I | E | | |

5. | | | I | E | |

6. | | | I | E | |

7. | | | I | E | | |

8. | | | I | E | | |

9. | | | | E | I | | |

10. | | | | E | I | |

11. | | | | E | I | | |

12. | | | | E | I | | | |

13. | | | | E | I | |

14. | | | | | E | I | | |

15. | | | | | E | I | | |

Spelling and Writing

Think of some things you'd like to buy. Jot down a few ideas on the lines below and then choose the most appealing item. On another sheet of paper, write the beginning of a manual that might come with the product. Explain the product's features, and tell how to use it. Use as many study words and additional study words as you can.

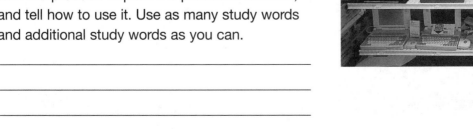

Words With /ī/

Study Words

tyrant
dye
shyness
dynasty
rye
dynamic
rhyme
dying
dyeing
hydrant
dynamite
typewriter
testify
ally
nylon

Additional Study Words

_____

_____

_____

_____

Spelling Rule

The sound /ī/ is the vowel sound in *ice*. It can be spelled in many ways. Three of these ways are *y*, *ye*, and *y* followed by a consonant and silent *e*.

Example:	y	ye	y-consonant-e
	ally	rye	rhyme

A. Say the Words

Say each study word. Notice whether /ī/ is spelled *y*, *ye*, or *y*-consonant-e. Then answer the questions below.

B. Write the Words

1. In which ten study words is /ī/ spelled *y*? Write the words. Circle *y* in each word.

_____   _____

_____   _____

_____   _____

_____   _____

_____   _____

2. In which three study words is /ī/ spelled *ye*? Write the words. Circle *ye* in each word.

_____   _____

_____

3. In which two words is /ī/ spelled with the *y*-consonant-*e* pattern? Write the words. Circle the *y*, the consonant, and the silent *e* in each word.

_____   _____

C. Add Study Words

Think of other words with /ī/ spelled *y, ye,* and *y-consonant-e.* Write these words below the study words list on this page. You might find new words on food packages, on billboards, and on labels.

Spelling and Language

A. Parts of Speech

Many words can be used as more than one part of speech, depending on how they are used in a sentence. For each sentence below, write the study word that fits in both blanks. Remember, a noun names a person, place, thing, or idea. A verb shows action or being. An adjective describes a noun.

Example: When I have just one *taste* of Mom's cookies, I have to *taste* ten.

(The first time *taste* is used, it is a noun. The second time it is a verb.)

1. These (adjective) stockings are made from a fiber called (noun).

   1. _____

2. The soldiers will (verb) the bridge, using sticks of (noun).

   2. _____

3. The weaver will (verb) the yarn, using red (noun).

   3. _____

4. The (noun) won't type dark letters until we change the (adjective) ribbon.

   4. _____

5. To write a (noun), you have to end the lines with words that (verb).

   5. _____

6. If you (verb) yourself with someone, then that person is your (noun).

   6. _____

7. (Adjective) bread is made out of a grain called (noun).

   7. _____

8. The (adjective) soldier's last words were, "I wish I were not (verb)."

   8. _____

9. I took a crafts class in (noun), and now I'm (verb) cloth in rainbow colors.

   9. _____

10. He is called a (adjective) king, because he rules like a (noun).

    10. _____

B. Related Words

Related words are words that share the same root or base word. Write one or more study words that are related to each pair of words below.

11. shy, shyly _____

14. dynamics, dynamo _____

12. dynastic, dynasties _____

_____

13. testifies, testifying _____

15. hydrate, hydration _____

Did You Know?

The word *tyrant,* which means "a cruel and oppressive ruler," comes from the Greek root *tyrannos.* In 1905, scientists used this same Greek root to name a huge, two-footed, flesh-eating dinosaur that had recently been discovered. They called the creature Tyrannosaurus rex.

Study Words

tyrant
dye
shyness
dynasty
rye
dynamic
rhyme
dying
dyeing
hydrant
dynamite
typewriter
testify
ally
nylon

Build Vocabulary

Read each group of words below. Decide which study word fits each category. Write it on the line.

1. poem, couplet, limerick

2. bread, flour, grain

3. bashfulness, caution, timidity

4. explode, detonate, blow up

5. kingdom, empire, throne

6. friend, pal, colleague

7. expiring, perishing, stopping

8. fire, hose, connection

9. oppressor, dictator, ruler

10. secretary, office, keyboard

11. color, stain, tint

12. upbeat, lively, energetic

13. tinting, painting, coloring

14. swear, explain, prove

15. rayon, cotton, wool

1. _____

2. _____

3. _____

4. _____

5. _____

6. _____

7. _____

8. _____

9. _____

10. _____

11. _____

12. _____

13. _____

14. _____

15. _____

Real-Life Spelling

Reading a Letter of Complaint

A letter of complaint usually describes a problem with a product or service and asks for help from the manufacturer or service company. If the letter is clear and reasonable, the writer has a good chance of being offered a repair or a refund. Read this letter of complaint. Find five misspelled study words. Write them correctly on the lines.

16. _____

17. _____

18. _____

19. _____

20. _____

April 15

Dear Color-Izer Company,

 I recently bought a package of your Color-Izer fabric die, because I wanted to change the color of my favorite shirt. I expected to get the dyenamic purple shade shown on the box. I can testifiy that I followed the directions for dying exactly, but my shirt hardly changed color at all. Maybe you should have said on the box that this product does not work on nilon. What can I do to get a better color?

 Sincerely,
 Luane Seitz

Spelling Review

Read each clue. Then complete the crossword puzzle with study words.

ACROSS

4. energetic
5. water hose connection
8. a poem whose lines have similar ending sounds
9. a succession of rulers in the same family
12. a strong synthetic fiber
13. a cruel ruler
14. say under oath in court

DOWN

1. an office machine
2. a powerful explosive
3. a friend
6. ending of life
7. coloring with dye
8. a kind of bread
10. bashfulness
11. a coloring for cloth

Spelling and Writing

Have you or someone you know been unhappy with a product you've bought? Think of a problem you've had with the product. Then jot down your ideas and follow up with a letter to the product's manufacturer. Describe the problem and ask how the company plans to solve it. Be polite and reasonable. Use as many study words and additional study words as you can.

Prefixes *non-* and *in-*

Study Words

nonsense
incorrect
nonfat
nonprofit
incomplete
nonfiction
inconvenient
nonscheduled
nonexistent
infinite
nonrefundable
injustice
nonstop
indestructible
nonviolent

Additional Study Words

_____

_____

_____

_____

Spelling Rule

The prefixes *non-* and *in-* can be added to many words. These prefixes mean "no" or "not" when they are added to the beginning of a base word. The spelling of the base word does not change when one of these prefixes is added.

Example:	Prefix		Base Word		New Word
	non-	+	sense	=	**non**sense
	in-	+	justice	=	**in**justice

A. Say the Words

Say each study word and look for the prefix *non-* or *in-* in each one. Then answer the questions below.

B. Write the Words

1. Which nine study words begin with the prefix *non-*? Write the words. Circle the prefix in each word.

_____   _____

_____   _____

_____   _____

_____   _____

_____

2. Which six study words begin with the prefix *in-*? Write the words. Circle the prefix in each word.

_____   _____

_____   _____

_____   _____

C. Add Study Words

Think of other words that begin with the prefixes *non-* and *in-*. Write these words below the study words list on this page. You might find new words in riddle books, schedules, and on lost and found notices.

Spelling and Language

A. Adding Prefixes

A prefix is a syllable added to the beginning of a word. It changes the word's meaning. When the prefix *non-* or *in-* is added to a word, it gives the word a negative or opposite meaning. Add *non-* or *in-* to the beginning of each word below to form a study word.

Example: in- + active = inactive   non- + stick = nonstick

1. fat _____

2. convenient _____

3. destructible _____

4. correct _____

5. fiction _____

6. finite _____

7. justice _____

8. sense _____

9. scheduled _____

10. profit _____

11. stop _____

12. complete _____

13. existent _____

14. violent _____

15. refundable _____

B. Alphabetizing

Alphabetizing words means putting them in order according to the letters of the alphabet. If the words begin with the same letter, look at the second letter in the words to see which comes first. If the first two letters are the same, look at the third letter, and so on. Alphabetize the following words and write them on the lines below: *nonfiction, nonprofit, nonrefundable, nonscheduled, nonexistent, nonviolent.*

Example: unaware, unfair, unfold, unkind, unknown, unwrap

16. _____

17. _____

18. _____

19. _____

20. _____

21. _____

> ### *Did You Know?*
> Some words have been in the English language for a very long time. The word *infinite,* which means "endless" or "unlimited," appeared in the writings of Geoffrey Chaucer, an English poet, in about 1380. He spelled it *infinit.* When you write it, don't forget to add the final *e*!

nonsense
incorrect
nonfat
nonprofit
incomplete
nonfiction
inconvenient
nonscheduled
nonexistent
infinite
nonrefundable
injustice
nonstop
indestructible
nonviolent

Build Vocabulary

Write a study word that completes each sentence.

1. _____ milk is healthier than whole milk.

2. It's _____ for me to practice on Mondays.

3. It's fun to imagine that dragons exist, even though I know that they are _____ .

4. The number of stars in the sky is _____ .

5. He can't give you your money back because the price you paid is _____ .

6. It's a terrible _____ when a criminal is found not guilty.

7. We are planning to gather in a peaceful, _____ demonstration.

8. When I say that your report is gibberish, I mean it's absolutely _____ .

9. The meal seemed _____ without dessert.

10. A _____ organization does good work but does not make money.

11. I gave so many _____ answers on my test that I asked to re-take it.

1. _____

2. _____

3. _____

4. _____

5. _____

6. _____

7. _____

8. _____

9. _____

10. _____

11. _____

Real-Life Spelling
Reading a Book Jacket

The back cover of a book jacket tells you something exciting about a book, and it gives you information about the author, too. Before you buy a book or take it out of the library, you can decide if you like it by reading the jacket. Read this book jacket and find five study words. Write them on the lines.

12. _____

13. _____

14. _____

15. _____

16. _____

Nonstop to Nowhere!

by José Lopez-Delgado

Fifteen-year-old José thought he was simply taking a flight to visit his father in Arizona, but was he incorrect! As a passenger on a nonstop, nonscheduled airline, he suddenly found himself involved in a serious misadventure. This nonfiction book takes you all the way from the wilds of Mexico to the Canadian Rockies. Readers will learn, along with José, just how indestructible the human spirit can be in the face of danger!

Spelling Review

Complete this puzzle with 14 study words that fit the clues below. When you finish, read the shaded column from top to bottom. The 15th study word will appear. Write it below the puzzle.

1. unending, uncountable
2. fat-free, low-calorie
3. not planned
4. imaginary, unreal
5. foolishness, gibberish
6. peaceful, calm
7. charitable, unpaid
8. unfair, wrong
9. factual, true
10. continuous, on and on
11. bothersome, annoying
12. final, not repayable
13. partial, insufficient
14. false, wrong

The 15th study word is _ _ _ _ _ _ _ _ _ _ _ _ _ _ .

Spelling and Writing

Examine some attractive book jackets to see where the title, author's name, and publisher's logo are shown. Then think of a book you enjoyed reading and design your own book jacket for it. First jot down some ideas below. Then use one side of a sheet of paper for the front cover. On the back, write an exciting paragraph that encourages people to read the book. Don't give away the ending! Use some study words and additional study words.

_____

_____

_____

_____

Words With /ōō/ and /yōō/

Study Words

unit
broomstick
cruiser
untrue
neutral
cartoonist
junior
nuisance
clueless
universe
blueprint
bruised
maroon
overdue
maneuver

Additional Study Words

_____

_____

_____

Spelling Rule

Many words have the sounds /ōō/ or /yōō/, the sounds you hear in the words *tool* and *unit*. These sounds can be spelled in many ways, including *oo, u, ui, ue,* and *eu.*

Example:	oo	u	ui	ue	eu
	br**oo**mstick	**u**nit	cr**ui**ser	overd**ue**	n**eu**tral

A. Say the Words

Say each study word and listen for the sound /ōō/ or /yōō/ in each one. Notice how /ōō/ or /yōō/ is spelled. Then complete the activity.

B. Write the Words

1. Write three study words in which /ōō/ or /yōō/ is spelled *oo.*

_____   _____

_____

2. Write three study words in which /ōō/ or /yōō/ is spelled *u.*

_____   _____

_____

3. Write three study words in which /ōō/ or /yōō/ is spelled *ui.*

_____   _____

_____

4. Write four study words in which /ōō/ or /yōō/ is spelled *ue.*

_____   _____

_____   _____

5. Write two study words in which /ōō/ or /yōō/ is spelled *eu.*

_____   _____

C. Add Study Words

Think of other study words that have the sounds /ōō/ and /yōō/. Write these words below the study words list on this page. You might find new words in a play, a novel, or a memoir.

Spelling and Language

A. Phonetic Spelling

The phonetic spelling of a word shows how the word is pronounced. Read the phonetic spelling of each study word below. Look for /ōō/ or /yōō/ in each word. Notice that some words have two accent marks. The longer mark shows the stronger stress. Then write the correct spelling for each one. For extra help, use the Pronounciation Key on page 107.

Example: (yōōn´ ə fôrm´) = uniform

1. (mə nōō´ vər) _____
2. (brōōm´ stik´) _____
3. (mə rōōn´) _____
4. (yōōn´ it) _____
5. (ō´ vər dōō´) _____
6. (krōōz´ ər) _____
7. (brōōzd) _____
8. (ən trōō´) _____

9. (blōō´ print´) _____
10. (nōō´ trəl) _____
11. (yōōn´ ə vʉrs´) _____
12. (kar tōōn´ ist) _____
13. (klōō´ lis) _____
14. (jōōn´ yər) _____
15. (nōō´ səns) _____

B. Regional Pronunciation

Some words are pronounced differently, depending on where you live in the United States. Each way is correct. Think about how you say each of the words below. Circle /ōō/ or /yōō/ according to which sound you say. Then write the words on the lines. Compare answers with your classmates.

Example: (sōōt´ kās) or (syōōt´ kās) = suitcase

Which do *you* say?

16. nuisance   /ōō/   or   /yōō/   16. _____
17. maneuver   /ōō/   or   /yōō/   17. _____
18. overdue   /ōō/   or   /yōō/   18. _____
19. neutral   /ōō/   or   /yōō/   19. _____

Did You Know?
You can make up clues for yourself to help you remember how to spell difficult words. For example, to remember how to spell the sound /ōō/ in *nuisance*, remember the sentence "You (*U*) and *I* are a *nuisance*."

Study Words

unit

broomstick

cruiser

untrue

neutral

cartoonist

junior

nuisance

clueless

universe

blueprint

bruised

maroon

overdue

maneuver

Build Vocabulary

In an analogy two pairs of words are related to each other in the same way. To complete an analogy, the words in the second pair must relate to each other in the same way as the words in the first pair. Complete each analogy with a study word.

Example: *Dog* is to *puppy* as *cat* is to *kitten.*

1. *Parent* is to *child* as *senior* is to _____ .

2. *Fact* is to *true* as *lie* is to _____ .

3. *Biased* is to *one-sided* as _____ is to *impartial.*

4. *Drawings* are to *painter* as *comic strips* are to _____ .

5. *Early* is to *beforehand* as *late* is to _____ .

6. *Map* is to *country* as _____ is to *building.*

7. *Conduct* is to *orchestra* as _____ is to *vehicle.*

8. *Navy* is to *blue* as _____ is to *red.*

9. *Bothering* is to *annoying* as *pest* is to _____ .

10. *Pebble* is to *beach* as *planet* is to _____ .

11. *Car* is to *convertible* as *ship* is to _____ .

12. *Cowboy* is to *horse* as *witch* is to _____ .

1. _____

2. _____

3. _____

4. _____

5. _____

6. _____

7. _____

8. _____

9. _____

10. _____

11. _____

12. _____

Real-Life Spelling

Reading a Thank-You Letter

A thank-you letter is written to show appreciation. You might receive a thank-you letter for a gift or some special help you gave. Read this thank-you letter. Find five study words to complete the letter. Write them on the lines.

13. _____

14. _____

15. _____

16. _____

17. _____

January 12

Dear Lieutenant Gordon,

I am very grateful to your mobile **(13)** for coming to the aid of my sister and myself after our auto accident last month. No cars passed for a long time, and we felt as if we were completely alone in the **(14)**. We were both badly **(15)**, and my sister even had a broken leg. I was **(16)** about how to help her. Then a police **(17)** arrived, and Officer Thompson knew just what to do. He helped my sister first, and he then helped me get the car safely off the highway.

Very gratefully,
Mary Hernandez

Spelling Review

Write each study word on the correct branch of this word tree. Notice other words that have /ōō/ or /yōō/ spelled the same way.

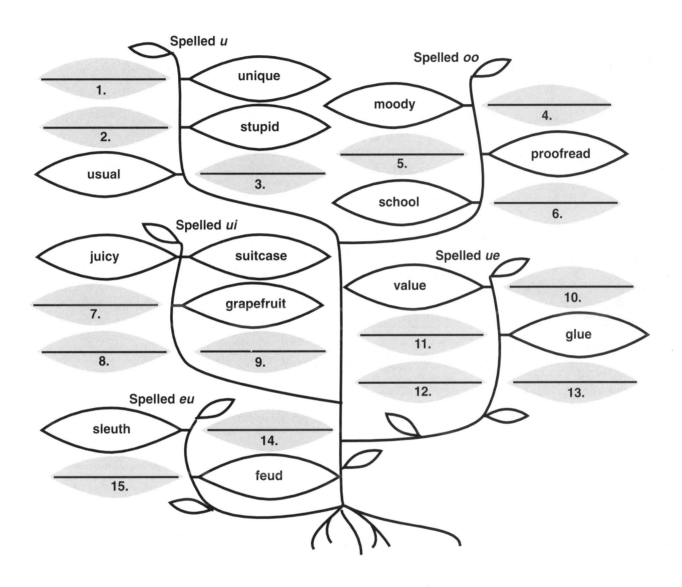

Spelled _u_
- unique
- stupid
- usual
- 1. _____
- 2. _____
- 3. _____

Spelled _oo_
- moody
- school
- proofread
- 4. _____
- 5. _____
- 6. _____

Spelled _ui_
- juicy
- suitcase
- grapefruit
- 7. _____
- 8. _____
- 9. _____

Spelled _ue_
- value
- glue
- 10. _____
- 11. _____
- 12. _____
- 13. _____

Spelled _eu_
- sleuth
- feud
- 14. _____
- 15. _____

Spelling and Writing

Think about a time when you, or someone you know, were helped by a friend, a family member, a teacher, or even a stranger. Jot down your ideas about what happened. Then write a thank-you letter to that person. Use as many of the study words and additional study words as possible.

Words With /sh/

Study Words

polish
insure
artificial
session
shuttle
discussion
glacier
mission
sheer
portion
ancient
surely
initial
pressure
edition

**Additional
Study Words**

_____

_____

_____

_____

Spelling Rule

The sound /sh/ that you hear at the beginning of the word *she* can be spelled in many ways. Some of those ways are *sh, s, ci, ss,* and *ti.*

Example:	**sh**	**s**	**ci**	**ss**	**ti**
	shuttle	**s**urely	an**ci**ent	mi**ss**ion	ini**ti**al

A. Say the Words

Say each study word and listen for the /sh/ sound. Look for the letters that spell the sound. Then complete the activity below.

B. Write the Words

1. Write three study words in which /sh/ is spelled *sh.*

   _____   _____

   _____

2. Write two study words in which /sh/ is spelled *s.*

   _____   _____

3. Write three study words in which /sh/ is spelled *ci.*

   _____   _____

   _____

4. Write four study words in which /sh/ is spelled *ss.*

   _____   _____

   _____   _____

5. Write three study words in which /sh/ is spelled *ti.*

   _____   _____

   _____

C. Add Study Words

Think of other words in which /sh/ is spelled *sh, s, ci, ss,* and *ti.* Write these words below the study words list on this page. You might find new words on book titles, on menus, and on newspaper headlines.

Spelling and Language

A. Phonetic Spelling

The phonetic spelling of a word shows how it is pronounced. Each phonetic spelling below contains the sound /sh/. Write the correct study word for each one. For extra help, use the Pronunciation Key on page 107.

Example: (shad´ ō) = shadow

1. (shut´ əl) _____

2. (sh͞oor´ lē) _____

3. (päl´ ish) _____

4. (mish´ ən) _____

5. (glā´ shər) _____

6. (pôr´ shən) _____

7. (ān´ chənt) _____

8. (sesh´ ən) _____

9. (shir) _____

10. (i nish´ əl) _____

11. (di skush´ ən) _____

12. (in sh͞oor´) _____

13. (presh´ ər) _____

14. (ē dish´ ən) _____

15. (ärt´ ə fish´ əl) _____

B. Related Words

Related words are words that share the same root or base word. Write the study word that is related to each group of words below.

Example: correct, incorrect, correction: correctly

16. discuss, discussing, discussed   **16.** _____

17. shuttled, shutttling, shuttles   **17.** _____

18. edit, edited, editing   **18.** _____

19. press, pressing, unpressed   **19.** _____

20. polishing, polishes, unpolished   **20.** _____

21. sure, assure, insured   **21.** _____

22. initially, initialed, initials   **22.** _____

> ### Did You Know?
> For hundreds of years, a *shuttle* has been the name of a weaver's tool that carries the thread back and forth quickly across the loom to make cloth. In 1895, the same word was first used to mean "a train that runs back and forth over a short distance." Now, *shuttle* also names another vehicle that goes on quick trips back and forth—to space!

Study Words

polish
insure
artificial
session
shuttle
discussion
glacier
mission
sheer
portion
ancient
surely
initial
pressure
edition

Build Vocabulary

Write the study word that completes each sentence.

1. That iceberg was once part of a _____ .

2. The _____ of my middle name is P.

3. The soldiers were sent on a secret _____ .

4. If you draw with more _____ , the lines you make will be thicker and darker.

5. The morning _____ of the newspaper said that schools will be closed today.

6. I was _____ sorry to hear that your grandmother was ill.

7. If the curtains are _____ , plenty of light will come into the room.

8. We had a long _____ about current events.

9. Food packages tell what a single _____ size is.

10. That argument we had is _____ history.

11. It's possible to _____ your home, your car, your health, and your life.

12. We shared ideas in our brainstorming _____ .

13. My uncle takes the _____ to his job.

1. _____
2. _____
3. _____
4. _____
5. _____
6. _____
7. _____
8. _____
9. _____
10. _____
11. _____
12. _____
13. _____

Real-Life Spelling

Reading a To-Do List

A to-do list comes in handy when you need to remember a lot of tasks, errands, or shopping items. Read this to-do list and find seven misspelled study words. Write them correctly on the lines.

14. _____
15. _____
16. _____
17. _____
18. _____
19. _____
20. _____

To Do This Week

Things to Buy:
furniture polesh
artifishial sweetener
single porshons of yogurt

Other:
pick up scheer curtains from cleaner
go to physical therapy seshon
have family discution about chores
inssure Greg's car

Spelling Review

Read the clues below. Then complete the crossword puzzle with study words.

ACROSS

1. huge body of ice
3. serious conversation
4. assignment
5. a part
6. rub until shiny
11. a period of activity
14. a space vehicle
15. certainly

DOWN

2. fake
7. protect against loss
8. urgent demands
9. very old
10. a publication
12. transparent
13. letter that begins a name

Spelling and Writing

What do you need to do in a typical week? Write a to-do list to help you remember. You might want to group together similar tasks under headings such as Errands, Things to Buy, and Appointments. First jot down some ideas below. Then on another sheet of paper, write a list. Use as many study words and additional study words as you can.

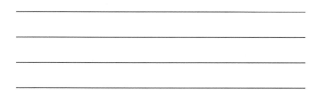

Contractions and Possessive Pronouns

Study Words

it's
its
you're
your
yours
they're
their
could've
ours
what's
we're
would've
should've
hers
let's

Additional Study Words

_____

_____

_____

_____

Spelling Rule

A contraction is a word in which an apostrophe takes the place of one or more letters that have been left out. A possessive pronoun is a word that shows ownership. It is not spelled with an apostrophe.

Example: **Contraction**   **Possessive Pronoun**
It's (It is) raining.   The dog licked **its** paw.

A. Say the Words

Say each study word and think about its meaning. Decide whether the word is a contraction and has an apostrophe that stands for letters that are left out, or is a possessive pronoun and shows ownership. Then answer the questions below.

B. Write the Words

1. Which nine study words are contractions? Write them. Circle the apostrophes in each word.

_____   _____

_____   _____

_____   _____

_____   _____

_____

2. Which six study words are possessive pronouns? Write each word.

_____   _____

_____   _____

_____   _____

C. Add Study Words

Think of other words that are contractions and possessive pronouns. Write these words below the study words list on this page. You might find new words in songs, poems, and stories.

Spelling and Language

A. Possessive Pronouns

A possessive pronoun is a pronoun that shows ownership. It has no apostrophe. In each of the following sentences, find the study word that is a possessive pronoun. Write it on the line.

Example: Here is *his* sweater. (The possessive pronoun is *his*.)

1. The dog soon tired of chasing its tail.

2. How did you know which house was ours?

3. I'd like to borrow your book to study.

4. Shelly thought the blue jacket was hers.

5. This bracelet is yours to keep.

6. The children finished their homework before going out to play.

1. _____

2. _____

3. _____

4. _____

5. _____

6. _____

B. Contractions

A contraction is a word in which an apostrophe takes the place of one or more letters when two words are combined. Read each sentence below. Then write the contraction formed by combining the underlined words. Each answer is a study word.

7. We are planning an Independence Day celebration.

8. When you are finished with your homework, call me.

9. They are having a sale on CDs and videos at the music store.

10. We would have enjoyed seeing the movie, but it was sold out.

11. He could have played in the game, but he forgot his cleats.

12. I should have studied more for the test.

13. Do you believe that it is already 4:00 P.M.?

14. Let us go swimming after the hike.

15. You have been reading for hours. What is the book about?

7. _____

8. _____

9. _____

10. _____

11. _____

12. _____

13. _____

14. _____

15. _____

> ### *Did You Know?*
> Contractions go back a long way. In the 1500s, the contractions for *she will* and *you will* were sometimes spelled *sheele* and *youle*. The apostrophe was added in the 1600s. In the word *won't,* the contraction for *will not,* the apostrophe doesn't seem to replace missing letters—until you learn that *won't* was first spelled *wynnot* and later *wonnot.*

it's
its
you're
your
yours
they're
their
could've
ours
what's
we're
would've
should've
hers
let's

Build Vocabulary

Read each clue below. Then write the study word that matches it.

1. could have

2. they are

3. let us

4. belonging to her

5. it is; it has

6. belonging to it

7. we are

8. belonging to you (four letters)

9. belonging to you (five letters)

10. would have

11. belonging to them

12. what is; what has

13. belonging to us

14. should have

15. you are

1. _____

2. _____

3. _____

4. _____

5. _____

6. _____

7. _____

8. _____

9. _____

10. _____

11. _____

12. _____

13. _____

14. _____

15. _____

Real-Life Spelling

Reading Book Titles

Book titles are the names authors give their books. Book titles often include contractions and possessive pronouns. Choose from the following seven study words to complete these book titles: *hers, what's, we're, let's, could've, their,* and *your.* Write the words on the lines below.

16. _____

17. _____

18. _____

19. _____

20. _____

21. _____

22. _____

(16) **Grow Tomatoes!**

You and (17) **Health**

(18) **Learning to Ski**

Songbirds and (19) **Nests**

(20) **Wrong With Our Air?**

I (21) **Been a Champion**

His and (22)

Spelling Review

Here's a puzzle without clues. Look carefully at the length and spelling of each study word. Notice which words have apostrophes and where the apostrophes appear in the words. Then figure out where each study word belongs in the puzzle. Some letters and all the apostrophes already appear in the puzzle. Each apostrophe has its own box.

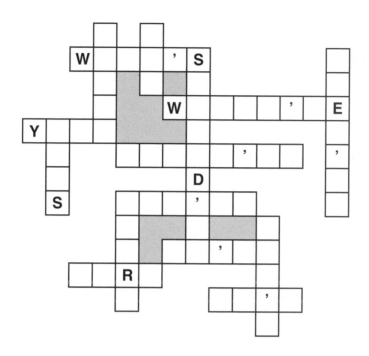

Spelling and Writing

What subjects interest you? On the lines below, jot down some topics you'd like to read more about. You might want to browse through books in your school library for ideas. Then on another sheet of paper, make up five book titles for one or more of your subjects. Use as many study words and additional study words as you can.

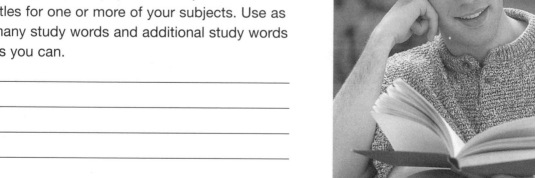

_____

_____

_____

_____

The Absorbed Prefix *ad-*

Study Words

adjust
accomplish
attempt
allies
approve
admission
attachment
assist
accumulate
assign
assemble
attendance
appliance
alliance
appreciation

**Additional
Study Words**

_____
_____
_____
_____

Spelling Rule

Many words begin with the prefix *ad-*. It means "to" or "toward." However, in words that would be hard to say if they began with *ad-*, the *d* in the prefix often changes to match the first letter of the root. Prefixes that change in this way are called absorbed prefixes.

Example: **ad**just   **ac**complish   **al**lies
           approve   **as**sign   **at**tempt

A. Say the Words

Say each study word and notice the spelling of the prefix in each one. Then complete the activity below.

B. Write the Words

1. Write two study words that begin with the prefix *ad-*.

_____   _____

2. Write two study words that begin with the prefix *ad-* spelled *ac.*

_____   _____

3. Write two study words that begin with the prefix *ad-* spelled *al.*

_____   _____

4. Write three study words that begin with the prefix *ad-* spelled *ap.*

_____   _____

_____

5. Write three study words that begin with the prefix *ad-* spelled *as.*

_____   _____

_____

6. Write three study words that begin with the prefix *ad-* spelled *at.*

_____   _____

_____

C. Add Study Words

Think of other words with the absorbed prefix *ad-*. Write these words below the study words list on this page. You might find new words on computer Web sites, in nonfiction books, and in catalogs.

Spelling and Language

A. Changing Verb Tenses

The past tense of a verb shows an action that has already happened. It often ends in -ed. The present participle of a verb shows continuing action. It takes a helping verb and ends in -ing. The present tense of a verb shows an action that is happening now. The verbs below are either past tense verbs or present participles. Write each verb in the present tense to form a study word.

Example: **Past tense**   **Present participle**   **Present tense**
stopped   is stopping   stop

1. accomplished _____
2. accumulated _____
3. assisted _____
4. approved _____

5. assigned _____
6. is adjusting _____
7. is attempting _____
8. is assembling _____

B. Noun-Forming Suffixes

A suffix is a word part added to the end of a word. When suffixes such as -ment, -ance, and -ion are added to some verbs, they form nouns. Write the noun that can be formed from each verb below. Each answer is a study word. Remember, sometimes the spelling of the base word changes when the suffix is added.

Example: **Verb**   **Suffix**   **Noun**
equip   -ment   equipment

9. attach _____
10. attend _____
11. admit _____

12. apply _____
13. appreciate _____

C. Guide Words

Guide words show the first and last entry words on a dictionary page. Write two study words that would appear on a dictionary page whose guide words are *alley* and *alligator*.

14. _____
15. _____

Did You Know?

Those big, puffy white clouds that look like heaps of cotton are called *cumulus* clouds. *Cumulus* is a Latin word meaning "a heap." The word *accumulate* is formed from the prefix *ad-*, "toward," plus the verb *cumulare,* "heap up." Whether you *accumulate* sports equipment or friends, it's as if you gather them toward yourself into a big heap.

adjust

accomplish

attempt

allies

approve

admission

attachment

assist

accumulate

assign

assemble

attendance

appliance

alliance

appreciation

Build Vocabulary

Think of a category for each group of words below. Then write the study word that fits each category.

1. collect, gather, acquire

2. connection, bond, tie

3. friends, co-workers, partners

4. like, praise, appreciate

5. admiration, attraction, recognition

6. confession, statement, announcement

7. help, aid, cooperate

8. gadget, tool, machine

9. treaty, agreement, cooperation

10. audience, congregation, assembly

11. gather, meet, put together

12. fix, correct, regulate

13. achieve, attain, finish

14. try, undertake, endeavor

15. appoint, nominate, delegate

1. _____

2. _____

3. _____

4. _____

5. _____

6. _____

7. _____

8. _____

9. _____

10. _____

11. _____

12. _____

13. _____

14. _____

15. _____

Real-Life Spelling

Reading a Service Order

A service order is a document that tells a repair person what work needs to be done. When a technician or a mechanic fixes something that doesn't work, he or she refers to this form. Read the service order from Vacuum Village, Inc. Find six misspelled study words and write them correctly on the lines.

16. _____

17. _____

18. _____

19. _____

20. _____

21. _____

VACUUM VILLAGE, INC.

SERVICE ORDER	No. _655668_

Customer Name _Mary Allison_

Location _1312 Joffrey Street_

Date _March 11_   Phone _555-7871_

WORK TO BE PERFORMED:

Customer says that dust and dirt seem to ackumulate in the vacuum hose. Check aplliance for low suction. Ajjust the fan and adtempt to vacuum living-room carpet. Fan seems to be faulty. Asemble and install a new fan mechanism, and try again. Finally, ascist customer by reviewing the use of vacuum parts.

Technician _Ginny Nguyen_

Time Started _4:15_ Time Finished _5:05_

Customer must approve work completed by signing below.

X _____

Spelling Review

Write each study word in the correct box of the web below. List the study words in each box in alphabetical order.

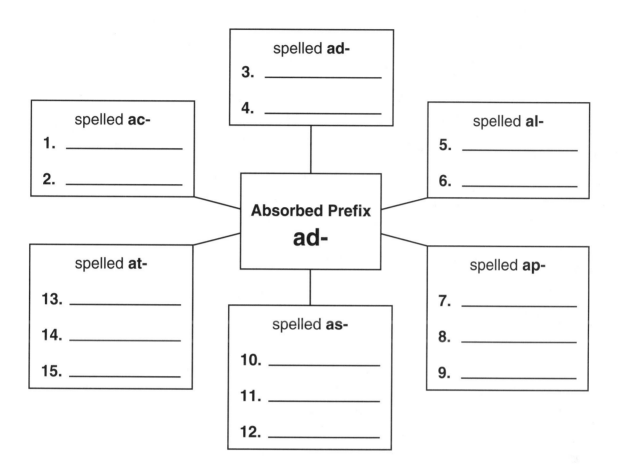

spelled **ad-**

3. _____
4. _____

spelled **ac-**

1. _____
2. _____

spelled **al-**

5. _____
6. _____

Absorbed Prefix ad-

spelled **at-**

13. _____
14. _____
15. _____

spelled **as-**

10. _____
11. _____
12. _____

spelled **ap-**

7. _____
8. _____
9. _____

Spelling and Writing

What needs to be fixed at your house? Write a service order for an item that needs to be repaired. It might be a refrigerator, a bike, or a TV. Jot down some ideas on the lines below. Then on another sheet of paper, write your service order. Be sure to tell what part doesn't work and why you need service. Use as many study words and additional study words as you can.

_____

_____

_____

_____

Unusual Plurals

Study Words

sixteen-year-olds
sheriffs
oxen
cupfuls
roofs
media
leftovers
species
onlookers
data
giraffes
bystanders
series
brothers-in-law
parentheses

Additional Study Words

_____
_____
_____
_____

Spelling Rule

Some plural nouns are unusual. Compound words often have oddly spelled plurals. Latin and Greek words follow those languages' rules for forming plurals. A few plurals are spelled the same as in the singular. Other plurals simply don't follow any rules.

Example: leftovers   media   series   oxen

A. Say the Words
Say each study word and notice how the plural is formed.

B. Write the Words

1. Write five study words that are plural compound nouns.

_____   _____

_____   _____

_____

2. Write three plural study words that come from Latin or Greek. These words change from *-um* to *-a* and *-is* to *-es*.

_____   _____

_____

3. Write two study words that are the same in the singular and plural.

_____   _____

4. Write three study words in which *f* or *fe* does not change to *v* before the plural ending is added.

_____   _____

_____

5. Write the study word formed by adding *-en* to a singular noun.

_____

6. Write the study word that ends in *fuls*.

_____

C. Add Study Words
Write other unusual plurals below the study words list. Look in instruction manuals, cookbooks, and science books.

Spelling and Language

A. Plural Nouns

A plural noun names more than one person, place, thing, or idea. Find the singular form of a study word in each sentence below and underline it. Then write its plural form on the lines.

Example: **Singular**   **Plural**
                teaspoonful   teaspoonfuls

1. I need a cupful of milk for this recipe.

2. He was a bystander who watched the strangers argue.

3. When people visit Africa, they hope to see a giraffe.

4. The onlooker seemed absorbed in watching the game.

5. The datum on the time of the event was important.

6. My brother-in-law is a sports fan.

7. Susan climbed on the roof to look for the bird's nest.

8. Write a parenthesis after each number in the list.

9. One ox is not as efficient as a pair.

10. The new sheriff was appointed, not elected.

11. The medium we most enjoy is television.

12. Can a sixteen-year-old get a driver's license?

13. Is this piece of lasagna a leftover?

1. _____

2. _____

3. _____

4. _____

5. _____

6. _____

7. _____

8. _____

9. _____

10. _____

11. _____

12. _____

13. _____

B. Same Spelling, Singular and Plural Nouns

Complete each sentence below with a study word whose singular and plural form is the same. You will write each word twice—once for the singular noun and once for the plural noun.

Example: Five *moose* crossed the road. Only one *moose* stopped to look at us.

14. John and I attended one game in each of the last three World _____. In last year's game, our favorite pitcher threw an amazing _____ of curve balls.

14. _____

   _____

15. Dozens of different _____ of ferns grow in the woods. My favorite _____ is one called rabbit's-foot fern.

15. _____

   _____

Did You Know?

Many people think that the word *media,* as in the expression "the news *media,*" is a singular noun. It isn't! There are several different news *media:* the *broadcast media* include television and radio, and the *print media* include newspapers and magazines. If you're talking or writing about only one, use the word *medium.*

sixteen-year-olds

sheriffs

oxen

cupfuls

roofs

media

leftovers

species

onlookers

data

giraffes

bystanders

series

brothers-in-law

parentheses

Build Vocabulary

Read each clue below. Then write the study word that matches it.

1. These are long-necked animals from Africa.

1. _____

2. Hurricanes can blow these off houses.

2. _____

3. People eat these for dinner when they're too busy to cook.

3. _____

4. Members of these cover the news.

4. _____

5. These animals can pull heavy wagons.

5. _____

6. These people enforce the law.

6. _____

7. These punctuation marks surround certain parts of sentences.

7. _____

8. Cooks measure flour and sugar using these.

8. _____

9. These are groups of related animals or plants.

9. _____

10. These people watch events, but they don't take part in them.

10. _____

11. These people stand nearby.

11. _____

12. These are sequences of things, such as games, events, or numbers.

12. _____

13. These are facts and figures entered into a computer.

13. _____

Real-Life Spelling

Reading a News Brief

A news brief is a short summary of the news. Late-breaking news for television must be written very quickly—sometimes even during an event! Read this news brief. Find six misspelled study words and write them correctly on the lines.

14. _____

15. _____

16. _____

17. _____

18. _____

19. _____

Four Sixteen-Years-Old Make News

The Murray quadruplets made headlines today when the three brothers and their sister received their driver's licenses. The quads have gotten so much attention from the medea that two sherifs made a presentation of the licenses in a ceremony. Onlookeres congratulated the quads, and even bystanderes stopped by. Mr. Murray's brother-in-laws will donate a used car for the quads to share. Stay tuned for interviews with the family.

Spelling Review

Thinking about a word's shape can help you remember how to spell it. Pay attention to tall letters, letters that hang below the lines, and the number of letters that are the same size. Study the word shapes below. Then write the study word that fits into each shape.

1.
2.
3.
4.
5.
6.
7.
8.
9.
10.
11.
12.
13.
14.
15.

Spelling and Writing

Think of an event at your school that might be reported on the local news. Jot down some ideas below. Then on a separate sheet of paper, write a news brief telling what happened. Use as many study words and additional study words as you can.

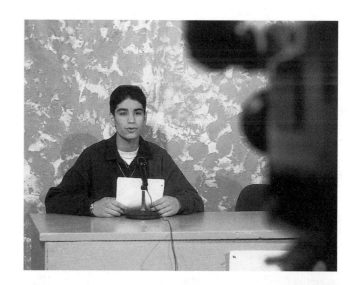

_____

_____

_____

_____

Study Words

detach
mistrust
detect
misjudge
defend
desirable
mistaken
deprive
misstep
departure
misfortune
decrease
mislead
misunderstood
demolished

**Additional
Study Words**

_____

_____

_____

_____

Spelling Rule

The prefixes *de-* and *mis-* often mean "away from," or "opposing." These suffixes can also mean "badly," "poorly," or "not." When *de-* or *mis-* is added to a base word or root, its spelling does not change.

Example:	Prefix		Base Word or Root		Word
	de-	+	tach	=	**de**tach
	mis-	+	trust	=	**mis**trust

A. Say the Words

Say each study word. Look for the prefix *de-* or *mis-* at the beginning of each word. Then answer the questions below.

B. Write the Words

1. Which eight study words begin with the prefix *de-*? Write the words. Circle the prefix in each word.

   _____   _____

   _____   _____

   _____   _____

   _____   _____

2. Which seven study words begin with the prefix *mis-*? Write the words. Circle the prefix in each word.

   _____   _____

   _____   _____

   _____   _____

   _____

C. Add Study Words

Think of other words with the prefixes *de-* and *mis-*. Write these words below the study words list on this page. You might find new words in advertisements, in guidebooks, and in cartoons.

Spelling and Language

A. Changing Verb Tenses

The past tense of a verb shows an action that has already happened. It often ends in *-ed*. The present participle of a verb shows continuing action. It takes a helping verb and ends in *-ing*. The present tense of a verb shows an action that is happening now. The verbs below are either past tense verbs or present participles. Write each verb in the present tense to form a study word.

Example: **Past Tense**   **Present Participle**   **Present Tense**
         stopped   is stopping   stop

1. is detaching _____

2. is misleading _____

3. defended _____

4. deprived _____

5. is decreasing _____

6. mistrusted _____

7. is misjudging _____

8. detected _____

B. Parts of Speech

A verb is a word that shows action or being. A noun names a person, place, thing, or idea. An adjective describes a noun. Read each part of speech and its word clue below. Then write the study word being described.

Example: **Part of Speech**   **Word Clue**   **Study Word**
         verb   separate   =   detach

9. verb; destroyed   9. _____

10. adjective; worth having   10. _____

11. verb; misinterpreted   11. _____

12. adjective; wrong   12. _____

13. noun; error   13. _____

14. noun; trouble   14. _____

15. noun; exit   15. _____

16. verb; unlatch   16. _____

Did You Know?

The job of a detective is to *detect,* or find evidence that helps solve crimes. One famous fictional detective is Sherlock Holmes, the main character in many mystery stories by the British author, Sir Arthur Conan Doyle. Holmes uses scientific methods to *detect* clues and solve crimes.

detach
mistrust
detect
misjudge
defend
desirable
mistaken
deprive
misstep
departure
misfortune
decrease
mislead
misunderstood
demolished

Build Vocabulary

In an analogy, two pairs of words are related to each other in the same way. To complete an analogy, the words in the second pair must relate to each other in the same way as the words in the first pair. Write the study word that completes each analogy below.

Example: *Toe* is to *foot* as *finger* is to *hand.*

1. *Built* is to *constructed* as *destroyed* is to _____ .

2. *Coming* is to *going* as *arrival* is to _____ .

3. *Guide* is to *lead* as *misguide* is to _____ .

4. *Right* is to *wrong* as *correct* is to _____ .

5. *Sell* is to *salesman* as _____ is to *detective.*

6. *Rise* is to *fall* as *increase* is to _____ .

7. *Peace* is to *trust* as *conflict* is to _____ .

8. *Good luck* is to *bad luck* as *fortune* is to _____ .

9. *Teacher* is to *educate* as *soldier* is to _____ .

10. *Connect* is to *disconnect* as *attach* is to _____ .

11. *Give* is to *contribute* as *take away* is to _____ .

12. *Print* is to *misprint* as *step* is to _____ .

1. _____
2. _____
3. _____
4. _____
5. _____
6. _____
7. _____
8. _____
9. _____
10. _____
11. _____
12. _____

Real-Life Spelling

Reading a Persuasive Essay
People often write essays to share their beliefs and opinions. In persuasive essays, writers try to convince readers of their point of view. Read this beginning of a persuasive essay. Identify six misspelled study words and write them correctly on the lines.

13. _____

14. _____

15. _____

16. _____

17. _____

18. _____

In Defense of Used-Car Salespeople

Used-car salespeople are among the most missunderstood workers in America. They are often thought of as business people who deliberately misleed their customers. There are even jokes about them. I would like to difend them against this prejudice because, in my opinion, most people misjuge them.

I admit, a few people who work at used-car dealerships would gladly sell you a car without telling you that it had been deemolished in an accident and then rebuilt. But there are a few "bad eggs" in every line of work. I believe that most of these men and women simply want to sell you a disirable, useful vehicle at a fair price.

Spelling Review

Part of each study word below is written in code. Use the symbols in the box to help you decode each one. Then write the completed words on the lines.

* = de -	# = mis -

1. * + fend   _____
2. # + taken   _____
3. * + molished   _____
4. * + prive   _____
5. # + step   _____
6. * + parture   _____
7. # + lead   _____
8. * + tach   _____
9. # + fortune   _____
10. * + sirable   _____
11. # + trust   _____
12. * + crease   _____
13. # + judge   _____
14. * + tect   _____
15. # + understood   _____

Spelling and Writing

Write an essay about a group of people you feel are being misjudged. Try to persuade your readers of your point of view. Tell how the people are being treated unfairly and explain why they do not deserve to be. Jot down some of your ideas below. Then on another sheet of paper, write your essay, or you may wish to write it on a computer. Use as many study words and additional study words as you can.

_____

_____

_____

The Absorbed Prefix *in-*

Study Words

inherit
illogical
immigrate
inexpensive
illegal
impolite
infection
irregular
immature
illustrate
imprison
improper
irrigate
illusion
irresponsible

**Additional
Study Words**

_____

_____

_____

_____

Spelling Rule

The prefix *in-* means "not" in some words and "in" or "into" in other words. In words that would be hard to say if they began with *in-*, the *n* changes to match the first letter of the base word or root. Prefixes that change in this way are called absorbed prefixes.

Example: *in-*   *il-*   *im-*   *ir-*
            inherit   **il**logical   **im**migrate   **ir**regular

A. Say the Words
Say each study word and notice the spelling of the prefix *in-* in each one. Then complete the activity below.

B. Write the Words
1. Write three study words that are spelled with the prefix *in-*.

_____   _____

_____

2. Write four study words in which the prefix *in-* is spelled *il*.

_____   _____

_____   _____

3. Write five study words in which the prefix *in-* is spelled *im*.

_____   _____

_____   _____

_____

4. Write three study words in which the prefix *in-* is spelled *ir*.

_____   _____

_____

C. Add Study Words
Think of other words with the absorbed prefix *in-*. Write these words below the study words list on this page. You might find new words in opinion surveys, business letters, and how-to articles.

Spelling and Language

A. Prefixes and Suffixes

A prefix is a word part added to the beginning of a word. A suffix is a word part added to the end of a word. Remove one prefix or one suffix from each word below to form a study word, but don't remove the prefix *in-* or its absorbed prefix forms. Write the study words on the lines. You may need to add or change a letter when you make this change.

Example:

Word	Prefix or Suffix	Study Word
imperfection –	-ion	= imperfect

1. imprisonment _____

2. immigration _____

3. irregularity _____

4. disillusion _____

5. improperly _____

6. disinherit _____

7. irresponsibly _____

8. illustration _____

9. irrigation _____

10. illogically _____

11. impolitely _____

B. Adjectives

An adjective is a word that describes a noun. Some adjectives precede the noun. Others follow it. Underline the adjective in each sentence below and write it on the line.

Example: That is an <u>enormous</u> cat. That dog is <u>small</u>.

12. That jewelry is inexpensive. 12. _____

13. The immature child cried to get away. 13. _____

14. The thief made an illegal entry into the house. 14. _____

C. Subject of a Sentence

The subject of a sentence is the noun or noun phrase that tells what or whom the sentence is about. Circle the noun in the subject in each sentence below. Then write it on the line.

Example: The (team) played well.

15. Her infection caused a high fever. 15. _____

16. An illusion is an unreal image. 16. _____

Did You Know?
When you spell words with absorbed prefixes, always add the whole prefix to the rest of the word. Don't omit one of the double letters where the prefix and the rest of the word meet. For example: *il- + logical, im- + mature, ir- + regular, as- + sign, ap- + prove.*

Study Words

inherit
illogical
immigrate
inexpensive
illegal
impolite
infection
irregular
immature
illustrate
imprison
improper
irrigate
illusion
irresponsible

Build Vocabulary

In some words, the prefix *in-* means "not." In other words, *in-* means "in" or "into." Read the clue in each item below. Write the study word that matches it.

1. Germs got *in* my cut. Now there is an _____.

   1. _____

2. Parking there is *not* lawful. It is _____.

   2. _____

3. I will put my money *in* the bank when I _____ it.

   3. _____

4. You're *not* acting your age. You're being _____.

   4. _____

5. The plan does *not* make sense. It's _____.

   5. _____

6. It's *not* good manners to shout. It's _____.

   6. _____

7. The CD did *not* cost a lot. It was _____.

   7. _____

8. You'll be thrown *in* jail. He will _____ you.

   8. _____

9. The pictures *in* this book _____ the story.

   9. _____

10. Jeanne will _____ to the United States when the officials let her *in*.

    10. _____

11. If you are _____, you're *not* trustworthy.

    11. _____

12. That tank top is *not* appropriate. It is _____ clothing for school.

    12. _____

13. Water will be piped *in* from the lake when we _____ the field.

    13. _____

Real-Life Spelling
Reading a Thesaurus

A thesaurus is a book in which synonyms are listed. Sometimes antonyms, or words that are opposite in meaning, are also listed. Writers often use a thesaurus to help them choose the exact words they need. Study these four thesaurus entries and find a study word in each one. Write the words below.

14. _____

15. _____

16. _____

17. _____

rude *adjective* discourteous, impolite, insulting, uncivilized, uncouth, vulgar. —*Antonym* considerate, courteous, polite, respectful.

deception *noun* apparition, delusion, dream, false impression, fantasy, illusion, mirage, misapprehension, phantom, vision. —*Antonym* certainty, fact, occurrence, reality.

old *adjective* ancient, antique, elderly, obsolete, prehistoric. —*Antonym* adolescent, childlike, immature, inexperienced, juvenile, modern.

abnormal *adjective* atypical, disorderly, exceptional, intermittent, irregular, lopsided, peculiar, strange, unusual. —*Antonym* customary, normal, standard.

Spelling Review

Find 15 study words hidden in this word search puzzle. They are spelled across, down, and on the diagonal. Circle the words. Then write them on the lines.

```
I  N  I  L  L  U  S  I  O  N  A  T  E  R  M
R  I  L  L  U  S  T  R  A  T  E  N  I  I  I
R  M  I  L  L  O  G  I  C  A  L  Y  R  L  N
I  M  M  A  T  U  R  E  L  L  L  E  R  L  E
L  I  P  L  L  I  M  P  O  L  I  T  E  U  X
L  G  R  I  M  P  R  I  N  H  E  R  I  T  P
O  R  I  G  A  T  E  I  N  H  E  G  I  T  E
G  A  S  I  R  R  E  G  U  L  A  R  A  R  N
A  T  O  L  I  R  R  I  G  A  T  E  O  L  S
E  E  N  A  L  I  M  P  R  O  P  E  R  T  I
I  I  N  F  E  C  T  I  O  N  I  O  N  E  V
I  N  I  R  R  E  S  P  O  N  S  I  B  L  E
```

1. _____   6. _____   11. _____

2. _____   7. _____   12. _____

3. _____   8. _____   13. _____

4. _____   9. _____   14. _____

5. _____   10. _____   15. _____

Spelling and Writing

Good writers often use both a thesaurus and a dictionary to help them select precise words for their writing. Look up the word *unlawful* in a thesaurus. On the lines below, list at least four synonyms for this word, including a study word. Check the definition of each synonym in a dictionary. Then on another sheet of paper, write a sentence for each word. Use as many study words and additional study words as you can.

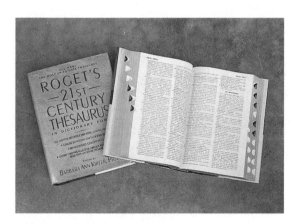

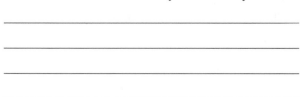

_____

_____

_____

_____

Study Words

extraordinary
superhuman
ultraviolet
superpower
extravagant
superlative
ultrasonic
supermarket
extraterrestrial
superficial
supersonic
ultramodern
superstar
extracurricular
superhighway

**Additional
Study Words**

_____

_____

_____

_____

Spelling Rule

The prefixes *super-*, *ultra-*, and *extra-* have similar meanings.
Super- means "above," *ultra-* means "beyond" or "extremely," and
extra- means "outside" or "beyond." When a word has one of these
prefixes, it describes something out of the ordinary.

Example: **super**human   **ultra**violet   **extra**ordinary

A. Say the Words

Say each study word and look for its prefix. Then answer the
questions below.

B. Write the Words

1. Which eight study words begin with the prefix *super-*? Write the
   words. Circle the prefix in each word.

   _____   _____

   _____   _____

   _____   _____

   _____   _____

2. Which three study words begin with the prefix *ultra-*? Write the
   words. Circle the prefix in each word.

   _____   _____

   _____

3. Which four study words begin with the prefix *extra-*? Write the
   words. Circle the prefix in each word.

   _____   _____

   _____   _____

C. Add Study Words

Think of other words that begin with the prefixes *super-*, *ultra-*, and
extra-. Write these words below the study words list on this page.
You might find new words in e-mail messages, science books, and
movie reviews.

Spelling and Language

A. Adjectives

An adjective is a word that describes a noun. Some adjectives begin with *super-, ultra-,* and *extra-.* Complete the word in each sentence below with an adjective that best describes the noun in italics. Each answer is a study word.

Example: This recipe calls for <u>superfine</u> *sugar*.

1. Jordan used super _____ *strength* to lift the car.
2. Sunscreen protects us from ultra _____ *light*.
3. They made an extra _____ *find* of an enormous gold nugget!
4. Pilots broke the sound barrier traveling at super _____ *speeds*.
5. The ultra _____ *building* looks like a tower of cubes.
6. In the movie, the extra _____ *aliens* had six arms.
7. Dan will surely get an A on his super _____ *essay*.
8. Five hundred roses is an expensive, extra _____ *gift*.
9. Dogs hear ultra _____ *sounds* that people don't.
10. I'm glad Jay's *injuries* were only super _____ .
11. My grades suffer because of too many extra _____ *activities*.

1. _____
2. _____
3. _____
4. _____
5. _____
6. _____
7. _____
8. _____
9. _____
10. _____
11. _____

B. "Super" Rhyming Couplets

Rhyming couplets are two-line poems that rhyme. Write the study word with the prefix *super-* that completes each rhyme below.

12. Hey, Mr. Basketball _____ ,
    We all know how great you are!

13. When a nation is a _____ ,
    It must be watchful every hour.

14. Use my car, but please don't park it
    Right in front of the _____ .

15. These days, on the _____ ,
    Nobody seems to be driving my way.

12. _____
13. _____
14. _____
15. _____

Did You Know?

The words *supersonic* and *ultrasonic* both contain the Latin root *sonare*, which means "sound." *Ultrasonic* refers to sounds so high-pitched that humans cannot hear them. *Supersonic* refers to the *speed* of sound. When a pilot breaks the sound barrier, he or she is traveling at *supersonic* speed, or faster than the speed of sound.

extraordinary
superhuman
ultraviolet
superpower
extravagant
superlative
ultrasonic
supermarket
extraterrestrial
superficial
supersonic
ultramodern
superstar
extracurricular
superhighway

Build Vocabulary

Write the study word that matches each definition below.

1. extremely modern   1. _____

2. large, self-service food store   2. _____

3. a creature from beyond Earth's limits   3. _____

4. outside of the regular school curriculum   4. _____

5. a mighty, influential nation   5. _____

6. faster than the speed of sound   6. _____

7. far beyond the ordinary   7. _____

8. past the end of the visible spectrum of light   8. _____

9. a star performer, as in sports or entertainment   9. _____

10. divided highway for high-speed traffic   10. _____

11. above the sound range that humans can hear   11. _____

12. superior to all others; the best   12. _____

13. greater than an ordinary human being   13. _____

14. on the surface; shallow   14. _____

15. costing or spending far too much   15. _____

Real-Life Spelling

Reading an Outline

An outline is a way to organize information. The main headings show the most important ideas. The subheadings show the supporting ideas. Read this outline based on an encyclopedia article about ultrasound and technology. Find five misspelled study words and write them correctly on the lines.

16. _____

17. _____

18. _____

19. _____

20. _____

> Ultrasound and Technology
> I. Using Ultrasound in Medicine
>   A. Shattering kidney stones
>   B. Checking internal organs
>   without surgery
>
> II. Using Ultrasonnic Waves in Dentistry
>   A. Drilling with suprelative
>   painless drills
>   B. Checking for tumors
>
> III. Ulltramodern Uses for the Future
>   A. Extrordinary techniques for
>   newborns
>   B. Suprhuman efforts to heal
>   damaged skin

Spelling Review

Each word below has the wrong prefix. Change the prefix to form one or two study words. Then write each word in the correct column of the chart.

1. extrahuman _____
2. supervagant _____
3. extramodern _____
4. ultraordinary _____
5. superterrestrial _____
6. superviolet _____
7. ultrapower _____
8. extraficial _____

9. extralative _____
10. ultrahighway _____
11. ultramarket _____
12. supercurricular _____
13. ultrastar _____
14. extrasonic _____
_____

super-
1. _____
2. _____
3. _____
4. _____
5. _____
6. _____
7. _____
8. _____

extra-
9. _____
10. _____
11. _____
12. _____

ultra-
13. _____
14. _____
15. _____

Spelling and Writing

Think of a topic you'd like to research. It might be the effects of ultraviolet light, the construction of a superhighway, or the life of your favorite superstar. Read about your topic and create an outline about it for an article. Use headings for main ideas and subheadings for supporting ideas. Include study words and additional study words in your outline.

Suffixes *-ment* and *-ship*

Study Words

township
refreshment
assortment
partnership
employment
leadership
engagement
argument
membership
placement
championship
management
scholarship
craftsmanship
adjustment

**Additional
Study Words**

_____

_____

_____

_____

Spelling Rule

The suffix *-ment* means "a product," "an action," or "the state of."
The suffix *-ship* means "the quality of" or "the condition of." The
spelling of a word usually remains the same when one of these
suffixes is added to it. However, there are a few exceptions, such as
the word *argue + -ment = argument*.

Example:	**Word**		**Suffix**		**New Word**
	employ	+	-ment	=	employ**ment**
	partner	+	-ship	=	partner**ship**

A. Say the Words

Say each study word and look for the suffix *-ment* or *-ship* in each
one. Then answer the questions below.

B. Write the Words

1. Which eight study words end with the suffix *-ment*? Write the
   words. Circle the suffix in each word.

   _____   _____

   _____   _____

   _____   _____

   _____   _____

2. Which seven study words end with the suffix *-ship*? Write the
   words. Circle the suffix in each word.

   _____   _____

   _____   _____

   _____   _____

   _____

C. Add Study Words

Think of other words that end with the suffixes *-ment* or *-ship*.
Write these words below the study words list on this page. You
might find new words on questionnaires, on photograph captions,
and in want ads.

Spelling and Language

A. Adding Suffixes to Verbs

A suffix is a word part added to the end of a word. It can change the word's meaning and part of speech. When the suffix -*ment* is added to some verbs, it forms nouns. Add -*ment* to each verb below and then write the noun you form. The spelling of one verb will change when the suffix is added.

Example: enjoy + -ment = enjoyment

1. refresh _ _ _ _ _____

2. adjust _ _ _ _ _____

3. argue _ _ _ _ _____

4. place _ _ _ _ _____

5. engage _ _ _ _ _____

6. assort _ _ _ _ _____

7. manage _ _ _ _ _____

8. employ _ _ _ _ _____

B. Adding Suffixes to Nouns

When the suffix -*ship* is added to a noun, it forms another noun. Add -*ship* to each noun below and then write the study word you form.

Example: owner + -ship = ownership

9. craftsman _ _ _ _ _____

10. partner _ _ _ _ _____

11. member _ _ _ _ _____

12. leader _ _ _ _ _____

13. town _ _ _ _ _____

14. scholar _ _ _ _ _____

15. champion _ _ _ _ _____

C. Guide Words

Guide words show the first and last entry words on a dictionary page. Write two study words you might find on a dictionary page whose guide words are as follows:

16. Guide Words: partly/plaid

16. _____

_____

17. Guide Words: adept/article

17. _____

_____

18. Guide Words: manage/membrane

18. _____

_____

Did You Know?
The word *scholarship* usually means "a gift of money to help a student pay for his or her education." But *scholarship* has another meaning—"excellence in academic work." If you display excellent *scholarship*, you might be offered an excellent *scholarship*!

Study Words

township
refreshment
assortment
partnership
employment
leadership
engagement
argument
membership
placement
championship
management
scholarship
craftsmanship
adjustment

Build Vocabulary

Think of a category for each group of words below. Then write the study word that fits each category.

1. job, career, work
2. village, community, municipality
3. snack, meal, food and drink
4. selection, mixture, variety
5. promise, commitment, betrothal
6. disagreement, fight, squabble
7. working together, companionship, cooperation
8. group, club, society
9. position, arrangement, rank
10. direction, rule, guidance
11. bosses, supervisors, administrators
12. first place, highest honor, winner
13. academic excellence, award, knowledge
14. workmanship, skill, talent
15. repair, alteration, change

1. _____
2. _____
3. _____
4. _____
5. _____
6. _____
7. _____
8. _____
9. _____
10. _____
11. _____
12. _____
13. _____
14. _____
15. _____

Real-Life Spelling Reading a Journal Entry

A journal is a daily record of events in the writer's life. People who write journals often record their thoughts and feelings about these events. Read this entry from DaQuan's journal. Then answer the questions with study words.

March 15

I had a REALLY good day today! The only uncomfortable moment was an argument I had with Jason about the soccer team. My counselor wants me to sign up for the advanced algebra test. She thinks I might be eligible for a math scholarship when I graduate from high school. Cool!

Jason and I made up after school. We even went to the soccer game together this evening. We met at the refreshment stand and sat with my brother and his girlfriend. They were holding hands and announced their engagement! I was so surprised! All in all, it was an exciting day.

16. What might DaQuan get when he graduates?
17. What did his brother and his brother's girlfriend announce?
18. What was the only uncomfortable part of the day?
19. At what kind of stand did DaQuan meet Jason?

16. _____
17. _____
18. _____
19. _____

Spelling Review

Find the study word that fits each clue. Write the words in the boxes from top to bottom. When you finish, read the shaded row of boxes from left to right. You will find the answer to the joke. Write your answer on the lines.

1. work that is for pay
2. winning first place
3. an unpleasant conversation
4. something to eat
5. location, position
6. people managing a business
7. a division of a county
8. a promise to marry
9. a gift of money to a student
10. all the people in a club
11. a variety of items
12. a jointly-owned business
13. a small change that fixes something
14. handiwork
15. the ability to take charge and guide others

Joke:

Piano Tuner: I'm here to tune your piano, ma'am.
Woman: But . . . but . . . I didn't call a piano tuner!

Piano Tuner: __ __ __ __   __ __ __ __ __ __ __ __   __ __ __!

Spelling and Writing

Write a journal entry about an especially interesting day in your life. Tell what happened and how you felt about it. Jot down some of your ideas below. Then on another sheet of paper, write the entry. Use as many study words and additional study words as you can.

_____

_____

_____

_____

Compound Words

Study Words

sweatshirt
side effects
beforehand
eyewitness
sign language
self-defense
homesick
masterpiece
know-how
shipwreck
touchdown
tape-record
handlebars
stopwatch
fire escape

**Additional
Study Words**

_____

_____

_____

_____

Spelling Rule

A compound word is made up of two words that are used as a single word. A *closed* compound word is written as one word. An *open* compound word is written as two words. A *hyphenated* compound word is joined by a hyphen.

Example:	**Closed Compound**	**Open Compound**	**Hyphenated Compound**
	sweatshirt	side effect	self-defense

A. Say the Words

Say each study word. Look for the two words in each compound word. Notice whether the word is a closed compound, an open compound, or a hyphenated compound. Then answer the questions below.

B. Write the Words

1. Which nine study words are closed compound words? Write the words.

   _____   _____

   _____   _____

   _____   _____

   _____   _____

   _____

2. Which three study words are open compound words? Write the words.

   _____   _____

   _____

3. Which three study words are hyphenated compound words? Write the words.

   _____   _____

   _____

C. Study Words

Think of other words that are compound words. Write these words below the study words list on this page. You might find new words in art books, fashion guides, and in sports magazines.

Spelling and Language

A. Compound Words

Match each word in Column A with a word from Column B to form a compound word that is a study word. Decide if the word is an open, closed, or hyphenated compound. Then write it on the line.

Column A	Column B	
1. eye	watch	1. _____
2. sweat	how	2. _____
3. side	escape	3. _____
4. fire	effects	4. _____
5. master	shirt	5. _____
6. know	bars	6. _____
7. touch	wreck	7. _____
8. stop	record	8. _____
9. handle	piece	9. _____
10. tape	sick	10. _____
11. ship	down	11. _____
12. home	hand	12. _____
13. before	defense	13. _____
14. self	language	14. _____
15. sign	witness	15. _____

B. Parts of Speech

Compound words can be different parts of speech. Read each part of speech and definition below. Then write the study word it describes.

16. verb; to record on tape	16. _____
17. adverb; ahead of time	17. _____
18. adjective; longing for your home and family	18. _____
19. noun; expertise	19. _____

Did You Know?

A *sign language* is a system of hand signals used to communicate. One of the most widely used sign languages is American Sign Language, or ASL, which was developed to be used by people who cannot hear. Today in the United States, American Sign Language is the fourth most commonly used language.

Study Words

sweatshirt
side effects
beforehand
eyewitness
sign language
self-defense
homesick
masterpiece
know-how
shipwreck
touchdown
tape-record
handlebars
stopwatch
fire escape

Build Vocabulary

Complete each sentence below with one or two study words.

1. It was hot, so I took off my _____ and tied it to the _____ of my bike.

2. An _____ across the street saw the man climb down the _____.

3. The football coach used a _____ to time Corey's _____.

4. I didn't know _____ that I was going to be so _____ at camp.

5. The composer went to a recording studio to _____ his _____.

6. The nurse used _____ to explain the medicine's _____ to the hearing-impaired patient.

7. The sea captain's _____ enabled him to avoid a terrible _____.

8. The man attacked the thief in _____.

1. _____

_____

2. _____

_____

3. _____

_____

4. _____

_____

5. _____

_____

6. _____

_____

7. _____

_____

8. _____

Real-Life Spelling

Reading a Fan Letter

A fan letter expresses someone's appreciation of another person's talent or performance. People often write fan letters to entertainers and sports stars. Read this fan letter that Jody sent to her favorite rock group, Shipwreck. Complete her letter with four missing study words. Write them on the lines below.

9. _____

10. _____

11. _____

12. _____

February 2

Dear Shipwreck,

I attended your concert in Orlando last weekend, and I thought it was an absolute __(9)__! It's a good thing I got my tickets __(10)__ by mail, because the box-office tickets were sold out within one day.

I wanted to __(11)__ the entire concert, but I know you never allow any taping or photography. I also tried to buy a T-shirt and a __(12)__ with your picture on them, but they were all gone before I got to the counter. I guess that just shows how popular you are in this state!

Thanks for a great concert. You're the best!

Sincerely,
Jody Clayton

Spelling Review

Read each clue below. Then, on the dashed lines, write the study word it describes. When you finish, read the circled letters from top to bottom. Write them below the puzzle. They will spell out a description of some of your study words.

1. outdoor stairway to escape fire _ _ _ _ _ _ ◯ _ _ _
2. language that uses signs _ _ _ _ ◯ _ _ _ _ _ _
3. skill _ _ ◯ _ - _ _ _ _
4. the remains of a wrecked ship ◯ _ _ _ _ _ _ _
5. to record on magnetic tape _ _ _ _ - ◯ _ _ _ _
6. steering bars with handles _ _ _ ◯ _ _ _ _ _ _ _
7. not the main effect _ _ _ _ _ _ _ _ ◯ _
8. ahead of time _ _ _ ◯ _ _ _ _ _ _
9. artwork made by a master ◯ _ _ _ _ _ _ _ _
10. a watch to time races _ _ _ ◯ _ _ _ _ _ _ _
11. longing to be home _ _ ◯ _ _ _ _ _
12. football play scoring six points _ _ ◯ _ _ _ _ _ _
13. one who sees something happen _ _ _ _ _ ◯ _ _ _ _
14. defending yourself _ _ _ _ - ◯ _ _ _ _ _ _
15. jersey shirt that absorbs sweat ◯ _ _ _ _ _ _ _ _

Some words are _ _ _ _ _ _ _ _ _ _ _ _ _ _ _ _ _ _.

Spelling and Writing

Think of a sports star or entertainer whose work you enjoy. Then write that person a fan letter. On the lines below, jot down ideas for what you'd like to say. Describe what you especially like about the star's work. Tell when and where you last saw him or her perform. Then on another sheet of paper, write your letter, using as many study words and additional study words as you can.

_____

_____

_____

Roots *nov* and *nom*

Study Words

novel
nominate
innovation
nominal
novelist
noun
nova
nominee
novelette
supernova
pronoun
renovate
novice
nomination
misnomer

**Additional
Study Words**

_____

_____

_____

_____

Spelling Rule

The Latin root *nov* means "new." The Latin root *nom* means "name." This root can also be spelled *noun*.

Example:	Root	Word	Meaning
	nov	in**nov**ation	the process of making changes
	nom	**nom**ination	the naming of a candidate
	noun	**noun**	the name of a person, place, thing, or idea

A. Say the Words

Say each study word and look for the root in each one. Then answer the questions below.

B. Write the Words

1. Which eight study words contain the root *nov*? Write them. Circle *nov* in each word.

   _____   _____

   _____   _____

   _____   _____

   _____   _____

2. Which seven study words contain the root *nom* or *noun*? Write them. Circle *nom* or *noun* in each word.

   _____   _____

   _____   _____

   _____   _____

   _____

C. Add Study Words

Think of other words that contain the roots *nov* and *nom.* Write these words below the study words list on this page. You might find new words on fliers, on Websites, and in written speeches.

Spelling and Language

A. Prepositions and Objects of Prepositions

A preposition shows the relationship between a noun and another word in a sentence. Some common prepositions are *by, for, from, of, on, about, after, before, inside, to,* and *with.* The object of a preposition is the noun that is described by the preposition. In each sentence below underline the preposition. Then circle the study word that is the object of the preposition. Write the circled word on the line.

Example: Tammy went to the (movie).

(The preposition is *to.* The object of the preposition is *movie.*)

1. Did you write a fan letter to a novelist?

1. _____

2. There were many characters in that novel.

2. _____

3. This hiking trail is too difficult for a novice.

3. _____

4. Astronomers study about what happens inside a nova.

4. _____

5. A person's name can be replaced with a pronoun.

5. _____

6. An adjective usually comes before the noun it describes.

6. _____

7. The election committee took calls for the nominee.

7. _____

8. How does a short story differ from a novelette?

8. _____

9. This magazine article is about scientific innovation.

9. _____

10. The light of a supernova appears bright this evening.

10. _____

11. The candidates were counting on Ann's nomination.

11. _____

B. Parts of Speech

A noun names a person, place, thing, or idea. A verb shows action. An adjective is a word that describes a noun. Read each part of speech and incomplete sentence below. Then write the study word that completes the sentence. Choose from the words *misnomer, renovate, nominate,* and *nominal.*

12. (verb) I plan to _____ John for president of the club.

12. _____

13. (adjective) There is a _____ fee to enter the museum.

13. _____

14. (verb) My uncle is planning to _____ an old house.

14. _____

15. (noun) The word *bear* is a _____ for a koala, because it's an Australian marsupial, not a bear.

15. _____

Did You Know?

A *nova* is an exploding star that hurls huge amounts of gas and dust into space. During such an explosion, a *nova* can be 10,000 to 100,000 times brighter than the sun. The brightest of these exploding stars is called a supernova.

Study Words

novel
nominate
innovation
nominal
novelist
noun
nova
nominee
novelette
supernova
pronoun
renovate
novice
nomination
misnomer

Build Vocabulary

Read each clue below. Then write the study word it describes.

1. person nominated for an elected office

2. part of speech that takes the place of a noun

3. repairing and modernizing an old house

4. long fiction story, usually arranged in chapters

5. short fiction story

6. star that brightens and then fades

7. to select someone to run for an elected office

8. star that is an especially bright nova

9. something called by the wrong name

10. word naming a person, place, thing, or idea

11. brand-new idea

12. relatively very small

13. new at something; beginner

14. the suggestion of someone for an office

15. writer of long fiction stories

1. _____

2. _____

3. _____

4. _____

5. _____

6. _____

7. _____

8. _____

9. _____

10. _____

11. _____

12. _____

13. _____

14. _____

15. _____

Real-Life Spelling

Reading Minutes of a Meeting

Many clubs have secretaries who take notes at meetings. These notes are called minutes. Minutes of one meeting are read at the next meeting, so that any mistakes can be corrected by the club members. Read the minutes of this book club meeting and complete them with six study words. Write the words on the lines.

16. _____

17. _____

18. _____

19. _____

20. _____

21. _____

Carlisle Book Club Minutes   May 15

The President called for the __(16)__ of candidates for new officers. Helen stood up to __(17)__ Barry for President and Juanita for Vice President. Ruthann suggested Peter as another __(18)__ for President, and Susan suggested Jody for Vice President.

The Treasurer asked everyone to pay a very __(19)__ fee as Club dues, since there is only $15.50 left in the treasury.

Jody led the discussion of the __(20)__ "Julie of the Wolves," by Jean Craighead George. We agreed that next we would read "Water Sky" by the same __(21)__.

The meeting was adjourned.

Jason Jankowski, Secretary

Spelling Review

Read the clues below. Then complete the crossword puzzle with study words.

Across

4. beginner
5. small or insignificant
7. new gadget or idea
10. long fiction book
11. word that replaces a noun
12. to suggest someone for office
13. a person suggested for office

Down

1. an author of novels
2. an extra-bright nova
3. to make new again
4. a star that brightens and then fades
6. the wrong name
8. a suggestion of someone for office
9. a short novel
12. word naming a person, place, thing, or idea

Spelling and Writing

Do you belong to an organization, such as a sports team, a book or music club, or a volunteer group? Think of things that might be discussed at a meeting of such an organization. Jot down some of your ideas below. Then on a separate sheet of paper, write a set of minutes. Use as many study words and additional study words as you can.

Study Words

bonanza
plateau
gondola
origami
parachute
salsa
bandanna
fatigue
broccoli
kosher
kindergarten
zucchini
monsoon
toboggan
banquet

Additional Study Words

_____
_____
_____
_____

Spelling Rule

Many words in English come from other languages. These words can be difficult to spell because they often follow the spelling and pronunciation rules of their original language. When in doubt, look up words from other languages in a dictionary.

Example:	Word	Language	Word	Language
	banquet	French	monsoon	Arabic
	broccoli	Italian	toboggan	Algonquian
	kindergarten	German	kosher	Hebrew
	bandanna	Hindi	origami	Japanese
	salsa	Spanish		

A. Say the Words

Say each study word. As you pronounce it, think about the number of syllables you hear in the word. Then complete the activity below. For extra help, use the Spelling Dictionary at the back of the book.

B. Write the Words

1. Write six study words that are made up of two syllables.

_____   _____

_____   _____

_____   _____

2. Write seven study words that are made up of three syllables.

_____   _____

_____   _____

_____   _____

_____

3. Write two study words that are made up of four syllables.

_____   _____

C. Add Study Words

List some words that you think might come from other languages. Check a dictionary to see if they really do. Write these words below the study words list on this page. You might see new words in restaurants, in clothing stores, and in supermarkets.

Spelling and Language

A. Adjectives

An adjective is a word that describes a noun. In each sentence below there is an underlined adjective. Circle the noun that it describes. Then write the word on the line.

Example: That is a <u>pretty</u> (hat) .   (*Pretty* is an adjective. It describes the noun *hat*.)

1. This is <u>spicy</u> salsa.   1. _____

2. My younger brother attends a <u>small</u> kindergarten.   2. _____

3. This <u>long</u> toboggan can hold six people.   3. _____

4. Josie wore a <u>red</u> bandanna around her neck.   4. _____

5. After the long hike, Marcie felt <u>great</u> fatigue.   5. _____

6. We ate lots of food at the <u>enormous</u> banquet.   6. _____

7. "<u>Easy</u> Origami" is the name of a paper-folding book.   7. _____

8. Mona asked me to pick the <u>ripe</u> zucchini.   8. _____

B. Plural Nouns

A plural noun names more than one person, place, thing, or idea. Many plural nouns are formed by adding *-s* to the singular noun. Read each plural noun below. Then write the singular noun from which it was formed.

Example: **Plural**   **Singular**
             toboggans   toboggan

9. monsoons _____   11. plateaus _____

10. parachutes _____   12. gondolas _____

C. Guide Words

Guide words show the first and last entry words on a dictionary page. Write two study words you might find on a dictionary page whose guide words are as follows:

13. Guide Words: kind/kowtow   13. _____

                                                    _____

14. Guide Words: bomb/brochure   14. _____

                                                    _____

Did You Know?

Origami is a Japanese word that means "to fold paper." It comes from two smaller Japanese words, *oru,* "to fold," and *kami,* "paper." In Japan, people enjoy folding paper boats, hats, boxes, flowers, birds, insects, and animals. There is a legend that if you are ill and you fold a thousand paper cranes, the gods might grant your wish to be well again.

Build Vocabulary

Read each clue below. Then write the study word it describes. The language from which each word comes is next to the clue.

Study Words

bonanza
plateau
gondola
origami
parachute
salsa
bandanna
fatigue
broccoli
kosher
kindergarten
zucchini
monsoon
toboggan
banquet

1. rain and wind (Arabic) 1. _____

2. high, flat, and grassy (French) 2. _____

3. sled (Algonquian) 3. _____

4. preschool (German) 4. _____

5. a source of wealth (Spanish) 5. _____

6. a colorful cotton square (Hindi) 6. _____

7. green vegetable with florets (Italian) 7. _____

8. green squash (Italian) 8. _____

9. according to Jewish dietary law (Hebrew) 9. _____

10. feast (French) 10. _____

11. paper-folding art (Japanese) 11. _____

12. used when jumping from a plane (French) 12. _____

13. boat used on canals in Venice (Italian) 13. _____

14. a spicy sauce (Spanish) 14. _____

15. exhaustion (French) 15. _____

Real-Life Spelling

Reading a Friendly Letter

In a letter to a friend or relative, the words you write are often like the words you speak. Contractions are used to take the place of two words, and you sign off with words like "*Love*" or "*Your friend.*" Read the following friendly letter. Find six misspelled study words and write them correctly on the lines.

16. _____

17. _____

18. _____

19. _____

20. _____

21. _____

Dear Aimee,

I'm having lots of fun in my garden. You should see me out here in the hot sun, hoeing away with a bandaina around my head. We're in a really dry spell, and I wish it would rain. At this point, I'd even take a monsune!

As you predicted, I've discovered that zuccini is a lot easier to grow than broccolly. I have so many cucumbers that Joe made pickles, but they're not as good as those kocher ones you brought us from the deli!

When you visit, we'll serve you a vegetable banquett.

Love,
Chris

60 Lesson 15

Spelling Review

Unscramble each set of letters below to form study words. Write the words on the lines. Then write the circled letters on the lines below the puzzle. They will tell you where all the study words are found.

1. QTNBAUE

2. OAAZNNB

3. GOOTANGB

4. EPUTAAL

5. LBBOORCIC

6. OOONNSM

7. CTUAAPRHE

8. AASLS

9. DLGNAOO

10. CZNHICIU

11. MGOAIRI

12. UFGAETI

13. DBNNNAAA

14. NRDNIEKARGET

15. HRSOKE

In the ___ ___ ___ ___ ___ ___ ___   ___ ___ ___ ___ ___ ___ ___ ___
        1   2   3   4   5   6   7   8   9 10 11 12 13 14 15

Spelling and Writing

Write a letter to a friend or relative. Tell what you are doing and how you feel about it. Use words that reflect the way you speak, and sign off with an informal closing, like *"Your friend"* or *"Love."* Jot down some of your ideas on the lines below. Then write your letter on another sheet of paper. Use as many study words and additional study words as you can.

_____

_____

_____

Roots *frac*, *gest*, and *cis*

Study Words

gestures
fraction
incision
digest
concise
fragment
precisely
fragile
decisive
congestion
fractured
digestion
incisors
refracted
suggested

Additional Study Words

_____

_____

_____

_____

Spelling Rule

The root *frac* means "to break." In some words this root is spelled *frag.* The root *gest* means "to carry" or "to bear." The root *cis* means "to cut." It is spelled *cise* at the end of a word.

Example:	Root	Word	Meaning
	frac	**frac**tured	broken
	frag	**frag**ment	piece
	gest	di**gest**	to summarize
	cis	in**cis**ors	cutting teeth
	cise	con**cise**	brief

A. Say the Words

Say each study word and look for the root in each one. Then complete the activity below.

B. Write the Words

1. Write five study words that contain the root *frac* or *frag.* Circle the root.

_____   _____

_____   _____

_____

2. Write five study words that contain the root *gest.* Circle the root.

_____   _____

_____   _____

_____

3. Which five study words that contain the root *cis* or *cise.* Circle the root.

_____   _____

_____   _____

_____

C. Add Study Words

Think of other words with the roots *frac, gest, and cis.* Write the words below the study words list on this page. You might find new words in newsletters, store fliers, and television commercials.

Spelling and Language

A. Parts of Speech

A noun names a person, place, thing, or idea. A verb shows action or being. An adjective describes a noun. Read each part of speech and clue below. Then write the study word it describes.

Example: noun; the outer covering of a tree (bark)

1. noun; a summary of information   1. _____
2. noun; piece of something that has been broken   2. _____
3. noun; a cut made by a surgeon   3. _____
4. noun; a number with a numerator and denominator   4. _____
5. verb; brought up as a possibility   5. _____
6. noun; front teeth for cutting   6. _____
7. adjective; short and to the point   7. _____
8. noun; hand movements   8. _____
9. adjective; easily broken   9. _____
10. adjective; bent, as a ray of light passing through water   10. _____
11. adjective; broken   11. _____
12. noun; the condition of being clogged up   12. _____

B. Prefixes

A prefix is a word part added to the beginning of a word. Adding a prefix can change a word's meaning. The prefixes *in-* and *im-* mean "not," and the prefix *de-* means "reverse the action of." Remove these prefixes from the words below to change their meanings. You will form study words. Write them on the lines.

13. indigestion   13. _____
14. indecisive   14. _____
15. decongestion   15. _____
16. imprecisely   16. _____

> ### Did You Know?
> *Incisors* are the teeth used by humans and other animals for biting. *Incisors* have straight, sharp cutting edges. Beavers' *incisors* have an orangish outer covering that is extremely hard. When a beaver gnaws wood with its *incisors*, the back part of the *incisors* that are not as hard, wear down faster than the front part. Because of this, their *incisors* keep a sharp edge.

gestures
fraction
incision
digest
concise
fragment
precisely
fragile
decisive
congestion
fractured
digestion
incisors
refracted
suggested

Build Vocabulary

Synonyms are words with the same or almost the same meanings. Write the study word that is a synonym for the word or phrase below.

1. exactly
2. piece
3. food breakdown
4. breakable
5. teeth
6. crowding
7. broken
8. signals
9. cut
10. bent
11. portion
12. eat
13. proposed
14. conclusive
15. brief

1. _____
2. _____
3. _____
4. _____
5. _____
6. _____
7. _____
8. _____
9. _____
10. _____
11. _____
12. _____
13. _____
14. _____
15. _____

Real-Life Spelling

Reading a Screenplay

A screenplay is the script from which a film is produced. It includes the actors' lines and may also include directions for the way cameras shoot the scenes. Read this short scene from a television movie called *General Surgery*. Find six study words in the script. Write them on the lines.

16. _____
17. _____
18. _____
20. _____
19. _____
21. _____

In the Operating Room

Dr. Kelley: *(glancing at Dr. Mandel)*
Why don't you do the honors, Dr. Mandel? Make the incision. And make it precisely.

(New Camera Angle—Dr. Mandel)

Dr. Mandel: *(glancing at nurse nervously)*
Scalpel, please. *She hands him the scalpel. He makes an incision in the patient's thigh.*

Dr. Kelley:
Whoa! Look at that fractured femur!

Dr. Mandell: *(sweating)*
There's…there's a sharp bone fragment dangerously close to the artery.

Dr. Kelley: *(sarcastically)*
And, John, now's the time for you to be decisive.

Dr. Mandell: *(grimly)*
Well, I don't think I'll use the procedure *you* suggested the last time I operated. We lost that patient, remember?

(New Camera Angle—Dr. Kelley)

Dr. Kelley: Actually, John, *you* lost that patient.

Spelling Review

Here is a puzzle without clues. Look carefully at the length and the spelling of each study word. Then decide which word belongs in each space. Some letters have already been added to the puzzle.

Spelling and Writing

Write a short scene for a movie. It can be a drama, a science fiction, or a comedy. Think of a plot. What's happening? To whom? Where? Why? First jot down some ideas for characters— how they interact, and what happens to them in the scene. Use as many study words and additional study words as you can.

Number Prefixes *mono-*, *bi-*, and *tri-*

Study Words

triple
bilingual
monogram
trillion
biceps
monoplane
binoculars
triplets
monopoly
binary
trio
monarch
triangle
monotonous
tripod

Additional Study Words

_____

_____

_____

_____

Spelling Rule

Many prefixes tell "how many." The prefix *mono-* means "one." It can also be spelled *mon-*. The prefix *bi-* means "two." It can also be spelled *bin-*. The prefix *tri-* means "three."

Example:	Prefix	Word	Meaning
	mono-	**mono**poly	control by one organization
	mon-	**mon**arch	king or queen
	bi-	**bi**lingual	using two languages
	bin-	**bin**oculars	field glasses with two lenses
	tri-	**tri**pod	three-footed

A. Say the Words

Say each study word and look for the prefix in each one. Then answer the questions below.

B. Write the Words

1. Which five study words begin with *mon-* or *mono-*? Write them. Circle the prefix in each word.

   _____   _____

   _____   _____

   _____

2. Which four study words begin with *bi-* or *bin-*? Write them. Circle the prefix in each word.

   _____   _____

   _____   _____

3. Which six study words begin with *tri-*? Write them. Circle the prefix in each word.

   _____   _____

   _____   _____

   _____   _____

C. Add Study Words

Think of other words with the prefixes *mono-*, *bi-*, and *tri-*. Write these words below the study words list on this page. You might find new words in game instructions, math books, and science books.

Spelling and Language

A. Alphabetical Order

Alphabetizing words means putting them in order according to the letters of the alphabet. If the words begin with the same letter, look at the second letter in each word to see which comes first. If these letters are the same, look at the third letter, and so on. Alphabetize each set of study words below.

Example: banana, band, bandanna, bandit

monoplane, monarch, monotonous, monogram

1. _____ 3. _____

2. _____ 4. _____

tripod, trillion, triangle, triple

5. _____ 7. _____

6. _____ 8. _____

bilingual, biceps, binoculars, binary

9. _____ 11. _____

10. _____ 12. _____

B. Syllables

A syllable is a part of a word that is pronounced with a single uninterrupted sound. You can hear a vowel sound in every syllable. Read the study words below and decide where the syllable breaks are. Then write each word in syllables on the lines. For extra help, use the Spelling Dictionary at the back of this book.

Example: mon o gram tri cy cle

13. biceps _____ **18.** trillion _____

14. triple _____ **19.** trio _____

15. triplets _____ **20.** bilingual _____

16. tripod _____ **21.** monopoly _____

17. monarch _____ **22.** triangle _____

Did You Know?
One, two, three, four, five . . . This is the way people count, but not the way computers count! We have ten fingers, so we use the base-ten system. But computers only need two digits—1 and 0. They use the *binary* system.

Study Words

triple

bilingual

monogram

trillion

biceps

monoplane

binoculars

triplets

monopoly

binary

trio

monarch

triangle

monotonous

tripod

Build Vocabulary

Write the study word that is related to each group of words below.

1. single, double, quadruple   1. _____

2. biplane, triplane, jet plane   2. _____

3. solo, duo, quartet   3. _____

4. trilingual, quadrilingual, multilingual   4. _____

5. twins, quadruplets, quintuplets   5. _____

6. million, billion, quadrillion   6. _____

7. triceps, quadriceps, pectorals   7. _____

8. rectangle, pentagon, hexagon   8. _____

9. base five, base ten, base twelve   9. _____

10. eyeglasses, telescope, magnifying glass   10. _____

11. boring, tedious, unvarying   11. _____

12. king, queen, emperor   12. _____

13. initials, decoration, embroidery   13. _____

14. corporation, controlling business, large firm   14. _____

15. camera, film, lens   15. _____

Real-Life Spelling

Reading an Advertisement

An advertisement is a public notice often found in a newspaper, a magazine, or the mail. It describes one or more products or services that are for sale. Many advertisements have attractive illustrations and catchy slogans. Read these advertisements and find five misspelled study words. Write them correctly on the lines.

16. _____

17. _____

18. _____

19. _____

20. _____

Healthy U Health Club

Build up those bicepts!

Membership only $50 per month

Stop by and try us free!

2468 Main Street
Call **555-PUMP**

Ice Cream Island

Specials this week:
• Banana Splits
• Trippol Dip Cones
• Fat-free Yogurt

Call 555-ICES

Charles Street Camera Shop

A trilion items for your camera!

Big Trippod Sale

Camera Cases
Digital Cameras
Film

**511 Charles St.
Call 735-8210**

Language Labs

Learn to speak Spanish!
Become bylingual in three weeks!

Call 555-0089.

Spelling Review

Find 15 study words hidden in this word search puzzle. The words are spelled across, down, and on the diagonal. Circle the words and then write them on the lines below.

```
T U V M O N O G R A M B I L I N G U A L
T R E O J O T Q E C O V I A T W R B Y U
F B I N A R Y N M O N A R C H R P I O I
R Z E O W W T U C X O A T U E L I C K M
Y T U P N I A C X R T R I A N P L P H G
T R I L L I O N Q Z O D Y U T R S P O D
Q I U A B I N L B I N O C U L A R S D D
U P U N C T Q M O N O P O L Y X E A G U
T L G E U R X U K S U M M O V F T N K R
D E S T R I P L E T S U T R I A N G L E
```

1. _____   6. _____   11. _____

2. _____   7. _____   12. _____

3. _____   8. _____   13. _____

4. _____   9. _____   14. _____

5. _____   10. _____   15. _____

Spelling and Writing

Think of a business where someone you know works and come up with a small advertisement for that business. Jot down a few ideas below. Then on a separate sheet of paper, write your advertisement. Use as many study words and additional study words as you can.

_____

_____

_____

_____

Suffixes *-age*, *-ity*, and *-tude*

Study Words

altitude
humidity
gratitude
shortage
attitude
identity
latitude
wreckage
minority
bandage
similarity
passage
majority
longitude
usage

Additional Study Words

_____

_____

_____

_____

Spelling Rule

When the suffix *–age* or *–ity* is added to a word or root, the spelling of the word or root does not usually change. However, if the word ends in *e*, the *e* is dropped before the suffix is added. When the suffix *–tude* is added to a word or root, it is often preceded by *i*.

Example:	Word	Suffix	New Word
	use	+ -age	= us**age**
	sincere	+ -ity	= sincer**ity**
	long	+ -tude	= longi**tude**

A. Say the Words

Say each study word. Look for the suffix *–age, -ity,* or *-tude* in each one. Then answer the questions below.

B. Write the Words

1. Which five study words contain the suffix *-age*? Write them. Circle *-age* in each word.

   _____   _____

   _____   _____

   _____

2. Which five study words contain the suffix *-ity*? Write them. Circle *-ity* in each word.

   _____   _____

   _____   _____

   _____

3. Which five study words contain the suffix *-tude*? Write them. Circle *-tude* in each word.

   _____   _____

   _____   _____

   _____

C. Add Study Words

Think of other words with the suffixes *-age, -ity,* and *-tude.* Write these words below the study words list on this page. You might find words on movie posters, in TV guides, and on first-aid kits.

Spelling and Language

A. Subject of a Sentence

The subject of a sentence is what or whom the sentence is about. Write the study word in the subject of each sentence below.

Example: The *team* played ball. (The subject of the sentence is *team.)*

1. The minority for four years was the Democratic Party.
2. The high humidity made the temperature seem hotter.
3. The wreckage lay by the side of the road.
4. A short passage led us out of the tunnel.
5. The ship's latitude was 45° N.
6. Our longitude was recorded at 107° E.
7. Correct English usage is important to be a good writer.
8. The water shortage was caused by lack of rain.
9. No similarity of any kind exists between us.
10. The altitude of the plane was 1,000 feet.
11. The majority of the passengers were not frightened.

1. _____
2. _____
3. _____
4. _____
5. _____
6. _____
7. _____
8. _____
9. _____
10. _____
11. _____

B. Direct Objects

The direct object of a sentence receives the action of the verb. It usually answers the question *"What?"* Read each sentence below. Underline the verb. Then find the study word that is a direct object. Write it on the line.

Example: Arnie <u>sliced</u> the *bread.* (The verb is *sliced.* The direct object is *bread.)*

12. Paul folded the bandage.
13. A rainy day affects my attitude.
14. Josie blamed the altitude for her discomfort.
15. A passport proves your identity.
16. You have my gratitude for all you did.

12. _____
13. _____
14. _____
15. _____
16. _____

Did You Know?

A system of imaginary lines on a globe or map can be used to find the location of any point on the earth's surface. Lines of *longitude* run from the North Pole to the South Pole. They indicate distance east or west of 0° longitude, the line of *longitude* that passes through Greenwich, England. Lines of *latitude*, such as the equator, run around the earth. A point's *latitude* is its distance north or south of the equator.

Suffixes *-age, -ity,* and *-tude*   **71**

altitude

humidity

gratitude

shortage

attitude

identity

latitude

wreckage

minority

bandage

similarity

passage

majority

longitude

usage

Build Vocabulary

Complete each sentence below with a study word.

1. The majority wins while the _____ loses.

2. Since a _____ of us voted for Todd, he won.

3. The _____ of the equator is 0°.

4. Locations on the earth are measured in latitude and _____ .

5. Wear a costume that will hide your _____ .

6. Explorers looked for a _____ to Hudson Bay.

7. High _____ keeps plants moist.

8. Her _____ improved when she got her way.

9. The plane is falling and we're losing _____ !

10. It is incorrect _____ to say, "I eats pizza."

11. Her cut was covered with a _____ .

12. Thankfulness is the same as _____ .

13. The _____ of food left everyone hungry.

14. When the plane crashed, they found the _____ .

15. My report shows a _____ to Simon's.

1. _____

2. _____

3. _____

4. _____

5. _____

6. _____

7. _____

8. _____

9. _____

10. _____

11. _____

12. _____

13. _____

14. _____

15. _____

Real-Life Spelling

Reading a Book Review

People read book reviews to learn about new books and to see if they want to read them. A book review provides interesting information about a book but it doesn't give away too much. It also gives the reviewer's opinion of the book. Read this book review. Find five misspelled study words and write them correctly on the lines.

16. _____

17. _____

18. _____

19. _____

20. _____

The Genius Who Discovered Longitude

by Dava Sobel

During the Age of Exploration, the world's most confusing scientific problem was how to determine a ship's lonjitude. The reckige of hundreds of vessels was adding up. Using an instrument called a sextant, sailors could figure out their lattitude. However, to determine longitude, they would also need a highly accurate clock.

In 1714, a large amount of money was offered to the first person who could build such a clock. In this book you will learn about the man whose persistent atatude led him to build it. However, as you will see, many of Britain's scientists were not exactly overcome with grattitude. Read the book to find out what happened!

Spelling Review

Complete the chart below. Start at the top of each column and work *downward*. Follow the directions to write each study word.

Words With - tude	Words With - ity	Words With - age
Write the word that begins with *long*. 1. _____	Write the longest study word. 6. _____	Write the word that means "not enough." 11. _____
Write its opposite. 2. _____	Write a weather term. 7. _____	Write the first-aid word. 12. _____
Reverse two letters. Write the new word. 3. _____	Write the word that means "most." 8. _____	Write the word that means "part of a book." 13. _____
Change one letter. Write the new word. 4. _____	Write its opposite. 9. _____	Write the word that means what's left after a wreck. 14. _____
Write the rhyming word of the word above. 5. _____	Write the word that begins with *i*. 10. _____	Write the shortest study word. 15. _____

Spelling and Writing

Choose a book you have read and feel strongly about. On the lines below, jot down some parts you liked or disliked about the book. Then on another sheet of paper, write a short book review. Your goal is to be informative, but don't give away the ending! Use as many study words and additional study words as you can.

_____

_____

_____

_____

Roots *cycle* and *meter*

Study Words

bicycle
meter
cyclone
thermometer
cycle
metric
encyclopedia
tricycle
millimeter
unicycle
meterstick
recycle
motorcycle
metronome
cyclist

**Additional
Study Words**

_____

_____

_____

_____

Spelling Rule

The roots *cycle* and *meter* come from Greek word parts. The root *cycle* means "circle," "ring," or "wheel." It is sometimes spelled *cycl.* The root *meter* means "measure." It can also be spelled *metr.*

Example:	Root	Word	Meaning
	cycle	bi**cycle**	two-wheeled vehicle
	cycl	**cycl**ist	a cycle rider
	meter	thermo**meter**	instrument to measure temperature
	metr	**metr**ic	a kind of measurement

A. Say the Words

Say each study word and look for the root in each one. Then answer the questions below.

B. Write the Words

1. Which nine study words contain *cycle* or *cycl*? Write them. Circle the root in each word.

_____ _____

_____ _____

_____ _____

_____ _____

_____

2. Which six study words contain *meter* or *metr*? Write them. Circle the root in each word.

_____ _____

_____ _____

_____ _____

C. Add Study Words

Think of other words with the roots *cycle* and *meter*. Write these words below the study words list on this page. You might see new words in bicycle stores, on road maps, and in museum displays.

Spelling and Language

A. Phonetic Spellings

The phonetic spelling of a word shows how it is pronounced. Read the the phonetic spelling of each study word below. Notice that some words have two accent marks. The longer mark shows the stronger stress. Write the correct spelling for each word. For extra help, use the Pronunciation Key on page 107.

Example: (sen´ tə mēt´ ər) = centimeter

1. (sī´ kəl)
2. (mēt´ ər)
3. (me´ trə nōm´)
4. (sīk´ list)
5. (sī´ klōn)
6. (en sī´ klō pē´ dē ə)
7. (mōt´ ər sī´ kəl)
8. (rē sī´ kəl)
9. (me´ trik)
10. (mēt´ ər stik´)
11. (thər mäm´ ət ər)

1. _____
2. _____
3. _____
4. _____
5. _____
6. _____
7. _____
8. _____
9. _____
10. _____
11. _____

B. Number Prefixes

A prefix is a word part added to the beginning of a word. Read the meanings of the number prefixes below. Then write the study word that matches each clue.

Prefix	Meaning	Prefix	Meaning
uni-	= one	tri-	= three
bi-	= two	milli-	= thousandth

12. a thousandth of a meter
13. three-wheeled vehicle
14. one-wheeled vehicle
15. two-wheeled vehicle

12. _____
13. _____
14. _____
15. _____

Did You Know?

Recycle means "to go around in a circle again," and when you *recycle* plastic bottles, glass jars, aluminum cans, and paper bags, that's exactly what you do! Instead of becoming garbage and going to a dead-end landfill somewhere, they're crushed, melted, or shredded back to their raw materials. Then they are used to make new containers, paper, and other useful things.

bicycle
meter
cyclone
thermometer
cycle
metric
encyclopedia
tricycle
millimeter
unicycle
meterstick
recycle
motorcycle
metronome
cyclist

Build Vocabulary

Write one or more study words that best fit each group below. Consider the word part that all the words in each group have in common. Use each study word once.

1. biped, bifocals, bicentennial

2. rebuild, recover, return

3. triplets, trilogy, trillion

4. motorbike, motorway, motorcade

5. artist, specialist, novelist

6. uniform, unique, united

7. yardstick, joystick, dipstick

8. enclosure, enchantment, encompass

9. bionic, magnetic, seismic

10. millipede, millisecond, millennium

11. thermonuclear, thermos, thermostat

12. metropolis, metrodome, metropolitan

13. metering, metered, meters

14. cycled, cycles, cycling

1. _____

2. _____

3. _____

4. _____

5. _____

6. _____

7. _____

8. _____

9. _____

10. _____

11. _____

12. _____

13. _____

14. _____

_____

Real-Life Spelling

Reading a Telephone Message

When you answer a telephone call meant for another person, it's helpful to write down a message for that person. Read this telephone message that Ashley wrote. Find four misspelled study words and write them correctly on the lines below.

15. _____

16. _____

17. _____

18. _____

November 3, 4 P.M.

Dad,

Mr. Bronson called. I told him you were out riding your motercycle, so he left a message. He says he sold you a meaterstick instead of a yardstick, but he's sure the directions for building the doghouse don't use the metrick system. I told him Queenie won't mind if her home is a millameter off, one way or the other. (Ha ha!)

Ashley

Spelling Review

Find 15 study words hidden in this word search puzzle. The words are spelled across, down, and on the diagonal. Circle the words and then write them on the lines below.

```
C H E M O T E R C Y U M E T
H Y M E T C L E R B C I T E
T F C T C Y U E E I I L E M
H C Y L Y C N N C Y Y L I E
E E M O E B I C Y C L I S T
R N E T R I C Y C L E M M I
M O T O R C Y C L E N E E R
O M R U N Y C L E P U T T C
M E O C Y C L O N E M E R Y
E S N X R L E P U T E R I C
T T O R M E T E R S T I C K
E E M E A T R D M E E I C Y
R R E C Y C K I L E R C Y C
A M E T O R E A C Y C L O R
```

1. _____   9. _____

2. _____   10. _____

3. _____   11. _____

4. _____   12. _____

5. _____   13. _____

6. _____   14. _____

7. _____   15. _____

8. _____

Spelling and Writing

Write a telephone message that someone in your family might need to take for someone else. Write it on a separate piece of paper. Be sure to include the date, the time, who called, and what that person said. Use as many study words and additional study words as you can.

Homophones

Study Words

claws
clause
stationary
stationery
hanger
hangar
patience
patients
wrapped
rapt
morning
mourning
flew
flu
flue

Additional Study Words

_____

_____

_____

_____

Spelling Rule

Homophones are words that sound alike but have different spellings and different meanings. You can tell which homophone to use by reading the sentence in which the word is found.

Example:	Homophone	Definition
	flu	infection caused by a virus
	flew	past tense of *fly*
	flue	chimney shaft

A. Say the Words

Say each study word and listen for groups of words that are pronounced the same. Notice the number of syllables in each group. Then complete the activity below. For extra help, look up the words in the Spelling Dictionary at the back of this book.

B. Write the Words

1. Write three groups of homophones that are one-syllable words.

_____   _____

_____   _____

_____   _____

_____

2. Write three pairs of homophones that are two-syllable words.

_____   _____

_____   _____

_____   _____

3. Write one pair of homophones that are four-syllable words.

_____   _____

C. Add Study Words

Think of other words that are homophones. Write these words below the study words list on this page. You might hear new words on the radio news, in rap songs, and on television commercials.

Spelling and Language

A. Parts of Speech

A noun names a person, place, thing, or idea. A verb shows action or being. An adjective describes a noun. Look at each part of speech and word clue below. Then write the study word being described.

Example: noun; the sound made by a dog (bark)

1. noun; garage for an airplane

1. _____

2. noun; first part of a day

2. _____

3. noun; chimney part

3. _____

4. noun; writing paper and envelopes

4. _____

5. verb; traveled through the air

5. _____

6. noun; curved nails on a cat

6. _____

7. noun; a frame to hang clothes on

7. _____

8. noun; a viral illness

8. _____

9. adjective; standing still

9. _____

10. noun; people who see a doctor

10. _____

11. verb; feeling sorrow after a loss

11. _____

B. Phonetic Spelling

The phonetic spelling of a word shows how it is pronounced. Homophones have the same phonetic spelling because they sound alike. Write two homophones for each phonetic spelling below. For extra help, use the Pronunciation Key on page 107 of this book.

Example: (dir) = deer   or   dear

12. (klôz) _____   _____

13. (pā´ shəns) _____   _____

14. (rapt) _____   _____

15. (stā´ shə ner´ ē) _____   _____

> ### Did You Know?
> The word *flu* is short for *influenza,* an Italian word that means "influence." *Influenza,* in turn, comes from the Medieval Latin word *influentia,* which means "flowing in." Why would an illness be called by this name? Ancient astrologers thought that diseases were caused by a mysterious fluid or power that flowed in from the stars!

Study Words

claws
clause
stationary
stationery
hanger
hangar
patience
patients
wrapped
rapt
morning
mourning
flew
flu
flue

Build Vocabulary

Complete each sentence below with the correct study word.

1. Your suit will wrinkle if you don't put it on a
_____ .

2. The doctor is not accepting any new _____ at
this time.

3. Sylvia was in _____ after her beloved dog died.

4. I was sick with the _____ last winter.

5. Is "to the party" a phrase, or is it a _____ ?

6. We opened the _____ before we used the
fireplace.

7. The _____ is Nick's favorite time of day.

8. I use _____ to write to my father.

9. I _____ Fluffy in a towel to dry him off.

10. The private jet is kept in its own _____ .

11. It was a windy day, so we _____ our kites on
the beach.

12. The traffic was so bad that Dana's car was
_____ for ten minutes.

1. _____

2. _____

3. _____

4. _____

5. _____

6. _____

7. _____

8. _____

9. _____

10. _____

11. _____

12. _____

Real-Life Spelling

Reading a Nature Log

A nature log is a kind of journal
or diary. Many nature lovers
keep logs in which they record
their observations of animals
and plants. Read the following
nature log entries. Complete
them with six study words.

13. _____

14. _____

15. _____

16. _____

17. _____

18. _____

11/7 6 A.M. I saw the bald eagle again. It sat at
the top of our bay tree for half an hour,
showing great (13) . It was watching the
surface of the lake.

11/7 5:30 P.M. The eagle returned to our tree.
It remained perfectly (14) for at least
fifteen minutes. When it (15) away, the
tree shook. Its body must be three feet long!

11/8 7 A.M. The eagle has not shown up yet
this (16) , but for once the lake is full of
jumping fish.

11/8 11 A.M. My eagle finally arrived. It is watching
the lake again with (17) attention.

11/8 11:15 A.M. That was awesome! It dived
down with its (18) extended, grabbed a
huge fish and took off.

Spelling Review

Read the clues below. Then complete the crossword puzzle with study words.

Across

1. cats' nails
2. an airport building
6. moved through the air
7. standing still
8. respiratory illness
9. ability to wait
10. doctors' customers
11. period of time before noon
12. being sad about a loss

Down

1. sentence part with a subject and verb
3. paying close attention
4. something to hang clothes on
5. covered in paper or other material
6. chimney shaft
7. letter paper and envelopes

Spelling and Writing

Write three entries for a nature log. Record your observations about a living thing, such as a pet or a flower. First jot down some ideas below. Then on a separate sheet of paper, write the entries. Use as many study words and additional study words as you can.

_____

_____

_____

Suffixes -ous and -ious

Study Words

conscious
nervous
ferocious
glamorous
religious
ambitious
generous
serious
numerous
unanimous
obvious
previous
superstitious
miraculous
unconscious

**Additional
Study Words**

_____

_____

_____

_____

Spelling Rule

Many words in English end in the suffix -ous. However, if the suffix is pronounced /jəs/ as in *religious*, /shəs/ as in *conscious*, or /ē əs/ as in *previous*, the suffix is spelled -ious. Use a dictionary, if you're not sure which spelling to use.

Example: **-ous**   **-ious**

numer**ous**   relig**ious**

gener**ous**   superstit**ious**

unanim**ous**   obv**ious**

A. Say the Words

Say each study word. Notice whether it ends with -ous or -ious. Then answer the questions below.

B. Write the Words

1. Which six study words end with the suffix -ous? Write them. Circle -ous in each word.

_____   _____

_____   _____

_____   _____

2. Which nine study words end with the suffix -ious? Write them. Circle -ious in each word.

_____   _____

_____   _____

_____   _____

_____   _____

_____

C. Add Study Words

Think of other words that end with -ous and -ious. Write these words below the study words list on this page. You might find new words on greetings cards, on thank-you notes, and on business fliers.

Spelling and Language

A. Adjectives

An adjective is a word that describes a noun. For each phrase below, write the adjective that describes the underlined noun. Each answer is a study word.

Example: a big <u>apple</u>   (The adjective is *big*. It describes the noun *apple*.)

1. an obvious <u>mistake</u> _____

2. the previous <u>day</u> _____

3. an unconscious <u>child</u> _____

4. a conscious <u>decision</u> _____

5. the unanimous <u>vote</u> _____

6. a miraculous <u>cure</u> _____

B. Comparative and Superlative Adjectives

For adjectives that are long words, write *more* before the comparative adjective and *most* before the superlative adjective. Complete each sentence below with the correct adjective. Each answer is a study word.

Example: **Comparative**   **Superlative**
             more delicious   most delicious

7. My most _____ friend goes to church every week.   **7.** _____

8. Lulu's injury is much more _____ than I thought.   **8.** _____

9. His angry dog is the most _____ in the neighborhood.   **9.** _____

10. I'm more _____ at night time because it's dark.   **10.** _____

11. This diamond is the most _____ gift I ever received!   **11.** _____

12. The wolf population is more _____ when food is plentiful.   **12.** _____

13. I know that Arnie is more _____ than his brother because he won't walk under a ladder.   **13.** _____

14. The most _____ people work night and day to get ahead.   **14.** _____

15. That beautiful movie star was even more _____ than her lovely sister.   **15.** _____

Did You Know?

The word *ambitious* comes from the Latin words *ambitus,* meaning "to go about," and *ambitio* meaning "a soliciting of votes." In Roman times, *ambitious* candidates for public office "went about" in their white togas, seeking votes. Today, an *ambitious* person is someone who has a strong desire for power and achievement.

conscious

nervous

ferocious

glamorous

religious

ambitious

generous

serious

numerous

unanimous

obvious

previous

superstitious

miraculous

unconscious

Build Vocabulary

Write the study word that describes each person or thing below.

1. someone who gives you a favorite possession   1. _____

2. someone with charm and beauty   2. _____

3. a vote in which everyone agrees   3. _____

4. someone who believes in omens   4. _____

5. someone who is not awake or aware   5. _____

6. someone who is anxious   6. _____

7. a fact that is very hard to miss   7. _____

8. someone saying prayers   8. _____

9. candles on the birthday cake of a 90-year-old   9. _____

10. someone who tries hard to get ahead   10. _____

11. a very grave situation   11. _____

12. someone fully awake and aware   12. _____

13. something that happened at an earlier time   13. _____

14. a wonderful event with no logical explanation   14. _____

15. a kind of animal that snarls and lunges   15. _____

Real-Life Spelling

Reading Interview Questions

News writers often conduct interviews to get information for their newspaper articles. They work from a list of questions they have prepared ahead of time. Read the questions that LaTrecia wrote before interviewing a hospitalized classmate for her school paper. Find seven study words and write them on the lines.

16. _____

17. _____

18. _____

19. _____

20. _____

21. _____

22. _____

> Interview with John Tinker
> New York Medical Center,
> February 11
> A) What caused such a serious
>   traffic accident?
> B) Did you have numerous injuries?
>   Were you knocked unconscious?
> C) Were you nervous about your
>   operation? Have you had any
>   previous operations?
> D) Were you conscious during the
>   operation, or did they give you
>   anesthesia?
> E) Your recovery seems miraculous.
>   How are you feeling now?

Spelling Review

Thinking about a word's shape can help you remember how to spell it. Pay attention to tall letters, letters that hang below the line, and the number of letters that are the same size. Study the word shapes below. Then write the study word that fits each shape. If two words have the same shape, write these words in alphabetical order.

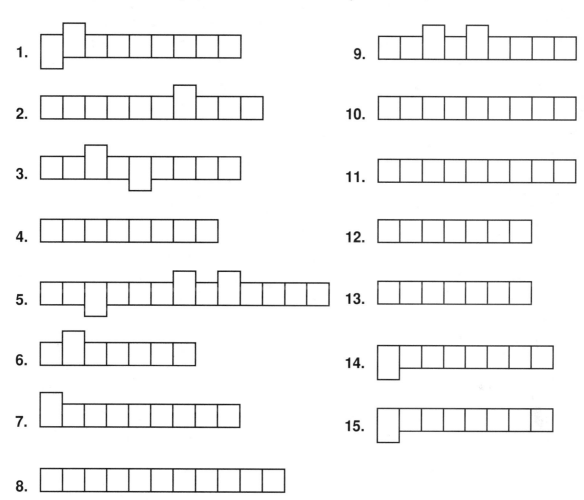

1.

2.

3.

4.

5.

6.

7.

8.

9.

10.

11.

12.

13.

14.

15.

Spelling and Writing

Think of someone you'd like to interview. The person could be a family member who has done something interesting or someone you'd like to learn more about. Jot down your questions below. Use as many study words and additional study words as you can.

_____

_____

_____

_____

Roots *gram* and *graph*

Study Words

biography
grammar
autograph
anagram
photography
grammatical
geography
telegraph
diagram
pictograph
telegram
graphic
hologram
programmer
bibliography

Additional Study Words

_____
_____
_____
_____

Spelling Rule

The roots *gram* and *graph* come from the Greek language. They both refer to "writing." *Gram* and *graph* can be found at the beginning, middle, or end of a word.

Example: grammar   **graph**ic
          pro**gram**mer   geo**graph**y
          dia**gram**   auto**graph**

A. Say the Words

Say each study word and look for the root *gram* or *graph* in each one. Then answer the questions below.

B. Write the Words

1. Which seven study words contain the root *gram*? Write them. Circle *gram* in each word.

_____   _____
_____   _____
_____   _____
_____

2. Which eight study words contain the root *graph*? Write them. Circle *graph* in each word.

_____   _____
_____   _____
_____   _____
_____   _____

C. Add Study Words

Think of other words with the roots *gram* and *graph.* Write these words below the study words list on this page. You might see new words in photography stores, in the post office, and in copy shops.

Spelling and Language

A. Plural Nouns

A plural noun names more than one person, place, thing, or idea. Many plural nouns are formed by adding -s to a singular noun. If a noun ends in *y,* the *y* changes to *i* before *-es* is added. Read each plural noun below. Write its singular form on the line.

Example: **Plural**   **Singular**
            soaps   soap
            candies   candy

1. anagrams _____

2. pictographs _____

3. diagrams _____

4. programmers _____

5. biographies _____

6. telegrams _____

7. autographs _____

8. holograms _____

9. graphics _____

10. bibliographies _____

B. Roots

A root is the basic part of a word. It gives the word its meaning. Add the root *gram* or *graph* to complete each study word below. Then write the word on the line. You will need to double the final consonant in *gram* to spell three study words.

11. dia_ _ _ _

12. _ _ _ _ _ atical

13. geo_ _ _ _ _ y

14. tele_ _ _ _ _

15. holo_ _ _ _

16. photo_ _ _ _ _ y

17. pro_ _ _ _ _ er

18. _ _ _ _ _ ic

19. _ _ _ _ _ ar

20. biblio_ _ _ _ _ y

11. _____

12. _____

13. _____

14. _____

15. _____

16. _____

17. _____

18. _____

19. _____

20. _____

Did You Know?

An *anagram* is the rearrangement of the letters in a word or phrase to spell another word or phrase. Amazingly, the letters in the words *eleven plus two* can be rearranged to spell *twelve plus one.* One of the study words, *telegraph,* can be turned into *great help!*

biography
grammar
autograph
anagram
photography
grammatical
geography
telegraph
diagram
pictograph
telegram
graphic
hologram
programmer
bibliography

Build Vocabulary

Read each definition below. Then write the study word it describes.

1. word whose letters can be rearranged to spell another word

2. realistic and vivid

3. science that deals with the earth's surface

4. someone who writes coded instructions for a computer

5. three-dimensional, laser-made picture of an entire object

6. graph that uses pictures to represent quantities

7. system for sending a message electrically

8. drawing that explains something

9. following the rules for speaking and writing

10. the story of someone's life

11. book list compiled by an author in writing a given work

1. _____

2. _____

3. _____

4. _____

5. _____

6. _____

7. _____

8. _____

9. _____

10. _____

11. _____

Real-Life Spelling Reading a Telegram

A telegram is a message sent by telegraph. Sending a telegram used to be the fastest way to send an urgent message, but today there are other ways. Because the price of a telegram is determined by the number of words in it, people use as few words as possible. Words such as *the, is,* and *a* are left out. No punctuation is used between sentences, and the word STOP is inserted to show that a sentence has ended. Read the telegram below. Find six misspelled study words. Write them correctly on the lines.

TELEGRAM

MARCH 19   8:44 PM   NEW YORK CITY

YOUR FIRST DRAFT OF PRESIDENT'S BIOGRAPHEY NOT VERY GRAMATTICAL STOP NONETHELESS CONTRACT FOR COMPLETION NOW BEING PROCESSED STOP WE NEED FOLLOWING THREE ITEMS STOP PHOTAGRAPHY FOR COVER STOP COMPLETE BIBLIOGRIPHY STOP ASSURANCE YOU WILL OUTOGRAPH BOOKS ON PUBLICITY TOUR BEGINNING JULY 15 STOP IF ACCEPTABLE PLEASE TELEGRAFF REPLY IMMEDIATELY STOP
YOURS TRULY KENSINGTON PUBLISHERS INC.

12. _____

13. _____

14. _____

15. _____

16. _____

17. _____

Spelling Review

Study the two word webs below. Then use the clues below the boxes to help you fill in the word webs with study words. Each answer contains the root *gram* or *graph*.

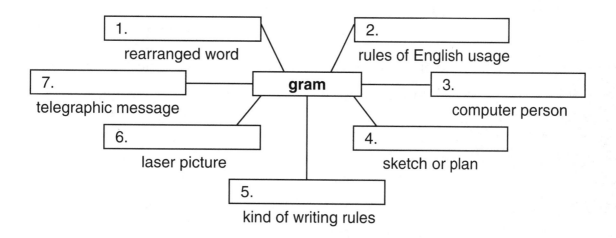

1. _____
rearranged word

2. _____
rules of English usage

7. _____
telegraphic message

gram

3. _____
computer person

6. _____
laser picture

4. _____
sketch or plan

5. _____
kind of writing rules

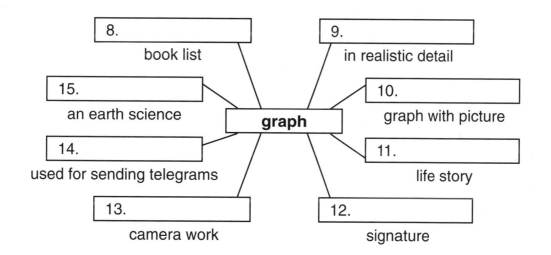

8. _____
book list

9. _____
in realistic detail

15. _____
an earth science

graph

10. _____
graph with picture

14. _____
used for sending telegrams

11. _____
life story

13. _____
camera work

12. _____
signature

Spelling and Writing

Write a telegram message to a friend or relative describing something wonderful or surprising that has happened. Remember to end each sentence with the word STOP instead of using a period. Omit small, connecting words. Use as many study words and additional study words as you can.

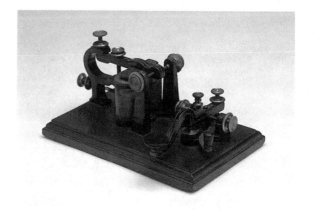

Roots *duct* and *sign*

Study Words

reduce
assignment
conductor
signify
reproduce
educator
resign
productive
significance
introductory
educational
designated
deduce
duct
designed

Additional Study Words

_____
_____
_____
_____

Spelling Rule

Hundreds of English words are based on the Latin roots *duct* and *sign*. The root *duct* means "to lead." In some words this root is spelled *duc* or *duce.* The root *sign* means "sign," "image," or "seal."

Example:	**Root**	**Word**	**Meaning**
	duct	pro**duct**ive	fertile
	duc	e**duc**ator	teacher
	duce	re**duce**	to lessen
	sign	as**sign**ment	a task

A. Say the Words
Say each study word and look for the root in each one. Then answer the questions below.

B. Write the Words

1. Which nine study words contain the root *duct*? Write them. Circle the root in each word.

_____   _____
_____   _____
_____   _____
_____   _____
_____

2. Which six study words contain the root *sign*? Write them. Circle the root in each word.

_____   _____
_____   _____
_____   _____

C. Add Study Words
Think of other words with the roots *duct* and *sign.* Write these words below the study words list on this page. You might find new words in editorials in the newspaper, on book jackets, and on school notices.

Spelling and Language

A. Adverbs

An adverb modifies a verb or an adjective. It can tell *how, where, how much,* or *when.* An adverb often ends in *-ly,* but not always. Read each sentence below with its underlined adverb. Write the study word that the adverb modifies.

Example: He <u>happily</u> sang the song. (*Happily* modifies the verb *sang.*)

This was a <u>more</u> interesting story. (*More* modifies the adjective *interesting.*)

1. Stripes on the sleeve of a uniform <u>usually</u> signify an officer.

2. Charlie stocked more shelves than I did, so he had a <u>more</u> productive day.

3. Abbie's medicine can <u>slightly</u> reduce her blood pressure.

4. Houses are <u>seldom</u> designed by the contractors who build them.

5. Mrs. Templeton's lecture was <u>very</u> educational.

6. Harry <u>carefully</u> designated the rivers on his map.

7. My work as chairperson is done, so I will resign <u>today</u>.

8. Will this copy machine <u>accurately</u> reproduce the page?

1. _____
2. _____
3. _____
4. _____
5. _____
6. _____
7. _____
8. _____

B. Related Words

Related words are words that share the same root or base word. Write the study word that is related to each group of words below.

Example: mechanic, mechanical, mechanics: mechanism

9. conduct, conducted, conductivity

10. introduce, introducing, introduction

11. assign, assigned, assigning

12. designate, designating, designation

13. signified, significantly, signify

14. educate, educational, education

15. ductile, ductless, ducts

16. deduced, deducing, deduction

9. _____
10. _____
11. _____
12. _____
13. _____
14. _____
15. _____
16. _____

> ### Did You Know?
> A *duct* is a tube or channel that carries something from one place to another. The ancient Romans built an amazing system of aqueducts, "ducts to carry water," to bring clean water to Rome from wells and springs outside the city. Their longest aqueduct was 57 miles long.

Study Words

reduce
assignment
conductor
signify
reproduce
educator
resign
productive
significance
introductory
educational
designated
deduce
duct
designed

Build Vocabulary

In an analogy two pairs of words are related to each other in the same way. To complete an analogy, the words in the second pair must relate to each other in the same way as the words in the first pair. Complete each analogy with a study word.

Example: *Finger* is to *hand* as *toe* is to *foot.*

1. *Confuse* is to *mix up* as _____ is to *figure out.*

2. *Gain* is to *increase* as _____ is to *decrease.*

3. *Designate* is to *appoint* as *indicate* is to _____ .

4. *Doctor* is to *physician* as *teacher* is to _____ .

5. *Flight attendant* is to *plane* as _____ is to *train.*

6. *Last* is to *first* as *final* is to _____ .

7. *Water* is to *pipe* as *air* is to _____ .

8. *Drawing* is to *sketched* as *building* is to _____ .

9. *Smallness* is to *insignificance* as *greatness* is to _____ .

10. *Asked* is to *invited* as *named* is to _____ .

11. *Give birth* is to *child* as _____ is to *offspring.*

1. _____
2. _____
3. _____
4. _____
5. _____
6. _____
7. _____
8. _____
9. _____
10. _____
11. _____

Real-Life Spelling

Reading a Humor Column

Newspaper columnists often have a good time making fun of today's lifestyles and culture. Read the beginning of this column from the entertainment section of a daily paper. Identify six study words and write them in the order you find them.

12. _____
13. _____
14. _____
15. _____
16. _____
17. _____

Useful Things We Learn From Movies

Did you ever realize how educational the movies can be? For example, we can learn about architecture. All buildings seem to be designed with a giant air-conditioning duct just above every ceiling. So all the trapped hero has to do is remove a vent and escape into a maze of ductwork.

I always pity the poor thugs who have the assignment of finding him. They have to resign themselves to running around in the rooms below. Of course, this isn't very productive, since they never get the good guy!

Spelling Review

Here's a puzzle without any clues. Look carefully at the length and spelling of each study word. Then decide which study word belongs in each space. Some letters have already been added to the puzzle.

Spelling and Writing

What strikes you as funny about today's world? Choose a topic related to team sports, movies, a tug of war, or another game. Jot down some ideas on the lines below. Then on another sheet of paper, write a short humor column. Use study words and additional study words.

_____

_____

_____

Study Words

odyssey
rhinestone
voltage
hamburger
pasteurize
bologna
panic
atlas
Braille
leotard
frankfurter
wattage
cashmere
galvanize
tangerine

Additional Study Words

_____
_____
_____
_____

Spelling Rule

Many English words come from the names of people and places. Sometimes a word's spelling is slightly different from that of the name it came from, and a few words from names are capitalized.

Example:

Name of Person	Word	Name of Place	Word
James Watt	wattage	Bologna, Italy	bologna
Jules Léotard	leotard	Rhine River	rhinestone
Louis Braille	Braille	Frankfurt, Germany	frankfurter

A. Say the Words

Say each study word. Decide whether the word is named for a person or a place. Then answer the questions below. For extra help, look up the words in the Spelling Dictionary at the back of this book.

B. Write the Words

1. Which nine study words come from names of people? Write them.

_____ _____

_____ _____

_____ _____

_____ _____

_____

2. Which six study words come from names of places? Write them.

_____ _____

_____ _____

_____ _____

C. Add Study Words

Use a dictionary to find other words that you think might come from the names of people and places. Write these words below the list of study words on this page. You might find new words in science books, on food labels, and on to-do lists.

Spelling and Language

A. Phonetic Spellings

The phonetic spelling of a word is part of a dictionary entry. It shows how the word is pronounced. Read the phonetic spelling of each study word below. Then write the correct spelling for each one. For extra help, use the Pronunciation Key on page 107.

Example: (spə get′ ē) = spaghetti

1. (vōl′ tij) _____

2. (äd′ i sē) _____

3. (pan′ ik) _____

4. (wät′ ij) _____

5. (at′ ləs) _____

6. (brāl) _____

7. (lē′ ə tärd′) _____

8. (bə lō′ nē) _____

9. (rīn′ stōn′) _____

10. (kash′ mir′) _____

B. Guide Words

Guide words show the first and last entry words on a dictionary page. Read the pairs of guide words below. Then write two study words that would appear on each of those dictionary pages.

Example: **Guide Words**   **Words on Page**

                       bog/branch   bologna, Braille

11. Guide Words: franchise/gamble   _____   _____

12. Guide Words: panhandle/pastime   _____   _____

13. Guide Words: volt/wave   _____   _____

C. Plural Nouns

A plural noun names more than one person, place thing, or idea. Most plural nouns are formed by adding -s or -es to a singular noun. Read each plural noun below. Then write the singular noun from which it is formed.

14. leotards _____

15. tangerines _____

16. atlases _____

17. rhinestones _____

18. hamburgers _____

19. frankfurters _____

Did You Know?

People who are blind can read by moving their fingers over patterns of raised dots that represent the letters of the alphabet. This writing system was created by a blind French boy, Louis Braille, who introduced it in 1824 when he was only 15 years old. Before Louis Braille's invention, blind people could not read at all. The system is called *Braille* in his honor.

odyssey
rhinestone
voltage
hamburger
pasteurize
bologna
panic
atlas
Braille
leotard
frankfurter
wattage
cashmere
galvanize
tangerine

Build Vocabulary

Read each clue below. Then write the study word it describes.

1. dance outfit; named after Jules Léotard

1. _____

2. to plate metal with zinc by using electricity; named after Luigi Galvani

2. _____

3. to destroy bacteria in milk and other foods by heating; named after Louis Pasteur

3. _____

4. small citrus fruit; named for the city of Tangier

4. _____

5. long sausage; named for the city of Frankfurt

5. _____

6. ground beef patty; named for Hamburg, Germany

6. _____

7. soft, combed wool; named for Kashmir, India

7. _____

8. glittery gemstone; named for the Rhine River

8. _____

9. measures of electrical power; named after the inventors Alessandro Volta and James Watt

9. _____

_____

10. long journey; named after the Greek hero, Odysseus

10. _____

11. nervousness; named after the Greek god, Pan

11. _____

12. writing system for the blind; named after Louis Braille

12. _____

13. smoked sausage; named for Bologna, Italy

13. _____

Real-Life Spelling

Reading a Poster

A poster is a large notice or sign that is used to publicize an event or important information. Read this poster and find six misspelled study words. Write them correctly on the lines.

14. _____

15. _____

16. _____

17. _____

18. _____

19. _____

LINCOLN SCHOOL RUMMAGE SALE

When: Saturday, April 9
3:00–6:00 P.M.

Where: In the gym

Hundreds of items for sale!
✔ Colorful atless of the world
✔ New dance leatord
✔ Cashmire sweater

Refreshments	
Hamberger	$2.00
Frankfooter	$1.50
Balony Sandwich	$1.00

Spelling Review

The study words below are written using the Braille alphabet. Decode the Braille letters into letters of our alphabet. Then write the words on the lines.

| A | B | C | D | E | F | G | H | I | J | K | L | M | N | O | P | Q | R | S | T | U | V | W | X | Y | Z |

1. __ __ __ __ __

2. __ __ __ __ __ __

3. __ __ __ __ __ __ __

4. __ __ __ __ __ __ __

5. __ __ __ __ __ __ __

6. __ __ __ __ __ __ __

7. __ __ __ __ __ __ __

8. __ __ __ __ __ __ __

9. __ __ __ __ __ __ __ __ __

10. __ __ __ __ __ __ __ __ __

11. __ __ __ __ __ __ __ __ __ __

12. __ __ __ __ __ __ __ __

13. __ __ __ __ __ __ __ __

14. __ __ __ __ __ __ __ __ __ __

15. __ __ __ __ __ __ __ __ __

Spelling and Writing

Create a poster to tell people about an event, such as a school play, or an important piece of information, such as safety at home and school. First, think of several ideas for your poster and jot them down. Then choose one idea and design your poster, using large letters and some illustrations. If your poster tells about an event, make sure to include the time and place. Use as many study words and additional study words as you can.

The Root *sist*

Study Words

persist
resistance
assistant
insistent
consist
resistant
persistent
resist
unassisted
subsist
consistent
insist
persistence
irresistible
inconsistent

**Additional
Study Words**

_____

_____

_____

_____

Spelling Rule

The Latin root *sist* means "to take a stand." This root can be found in the middle or at the end of a word.

Example:	**Root at the End**	**Root in the Middle**
	per**sist**	per**sist**ent
	re**sist**	irre**sist**ible
	con**sist**	incon**sist**ent

A. Say the Words

Say each study word and look for the root *sist*. Notice the different prefixes and suffixes that have been added to the root. Then answer the questions below.

B. Write the Words

1. Which five study words are made up of *sist* plus a prefix? Write them. Circle *sist* in each word.

   _____   _____

   _____   _____

   _____

2. Which seven study words are made up of *sist* plus a prefix and a suffix? Write them. Circle *sist* in each word.

   _____   _____

   _____   _____

   _____   _____

   _____

3. Which three study words are made up of *sist* plus two prefixes and a suffix? Write them. Circle *sist* in each word.

   _____   _____

   _____

C. Add Study Words

Think of other words with the root *sist*. Write these words below the list of study words on this page. You might find new words on business letters, in self-help books, and in newspaper columns.

Spelling and Language

A. Roots

A root is the basic part of a word. It gives the word its meaning. Complete each study word below with the root *sist*. Then write the word on the line.

1. con _ _ _ _

2. in _ _ _ _

3. in _ _ _ _ ent

4. unas _ _ _ _ ed

5. as _ _ _ _ ant

6. re _ _ _ _

7. irre _ _ _ _ ible

8. re _ _ _ _ ant

9. re _ _ _ _ ance

10. sub _ _ _ _

11. con _ _ _ _ ent

12. incon _ _ _ _ ent

1. _____

2. _____

3. _____

4. _____

5. _____

6. _____

7. _____

8. _____

9. _____

10. _____

11. _____

12. _____

B. Alphabetizing

Alphabetizing words means putting them in order according to the letters of the alphabet. If two words begin with the same letter, look at the second letter in the words to see which comes first. If the first two letters are the same, look at the third letter, and so on. Alphabetize each set of study words below. Write them on the lines.

Example: returnable, returned, returning

resistance, resist, resistant

13. _____   14. _____   15. _____

persistent, persistence, persist

16. _____   17. _____   18. _____

> ### Did You Know?
> The word *persistence* means "to continue to exist or endure." The Spanish artist Salvador Dali used the word in the title of his most famous painting, "The Persistence of Memory." In this dreamlike painting, completed in 1931, drooping clocks hang over the branches of bare trees in a strange desert. The artist was trying to say that memories can last a long time.

Study Words

persist
resistance
assistant
insistent
consist
resistant
persistent
resist
unassisted
subsist
consistent
insist
persistence
irresistible
inconsistent

Build Vocabulary

Read each definition below. Then write the study word that matches it.

1. not compatible with other facts   1. _____
2. to oppose something   2. _____
3. to continue to exist   3. _____
4. in agreement   4. _____
5. demanding   5. _____
6. to refuse to give up, to endure   6. _____
7. something that cannot be resisted   7. _____
8. to be formed or made up of   8. _____
9. helper   9. _____
10. showing opposition to   10. _____
11. to demand strongly   11. _____
12. not aided   12. _____
13. perseverance   13. _____
14. the power to resist   14. _____

Real-Life Spelling

Reading a Limerick

A limerick is a funny, five-line poem that always follows the same rhyming pattern. The first, second, and fifth lines rhyme, and the third and fourth lines rhyme. Limericks are found in books of riddles and poems. This form of poetry is more than a hundred years old! Read this limerick and find three study words. Write them on the lines.

15. _____
16. _____
17. _____

LIMERICK

The boss was extremely insistent
That he must have an office assistant.
But he worked at a pool,
So he posted the rule
That she'd have to be water resistant!

Spelling Review

Read the prefix at the top of each box. Then write each study word under its correct prefix. Three study words have two prefixes. Write those words in two places.

as-

1. _____

2. _____

con-

3. _____

4. _____

5. _____

in- or ir-

6. _____

7. _____

8. _____

9. _____

per-

10. _____

11. _____

12. _____

re-

13. _____

14. _____

15. _____

16. _____

sub-

17. _____

un-

18. _____

Spelling and Writing

Write a limerick or another short, funny poem. First think of a topic for your poem, such as "Fun Times." Write it on the lines below. Jot down groups of words that rhyme too. Then on another sheet of paper, write your poem. Reread the limerick on page 100 to recall the rhyming pattern. Use as many study words and additional study words as you can.

_____

_____

_____

_____

Spelling and Pronunciation

Study Words

vegetable
lightning
miniature
athletics
restaurant
ecstatic
tentative
aspirin
chocolate
penetrate
foliage
temperature
separate
twelfth
mischievous

Additional Study Words

_____
_____
_____
_____

Spelling Rule

Some words are often mispronounced or carelessly pronounced. Sometimes extra sounds are added to words. At other times sounds are left out. These pronunciation mistakes make the words difficult to spell. You may need to look up their pronunciations in a dictionary.

Example: **Often-Mispronounced Words**
mischievous   twelfth   aspirin

A. Say the Words

Say each study word and look carefully at its spelling. Listen for the number of syllables in each word. Then complete the activity below. For extra help, look up the words in the Spelling Dictionary at the back of this book.

B. Write the Words

1. Write the only study word that is made up of one syllable.

_____

2. Write the only study word that is made up of two syllables.

_____

3. Write ten study words that are made up of three syllables.

_____   _____

_____   _____

_____   _____

_____   _____

_____   _____

4. Write three study words that are made up of four syllables.

_____   _____

_____

C. Add Study Words

Think of other words that are often mispronounced and therefore hard to spell. Write these words below the study words list on this page. You might find new words in recipes, in vacation brochures, and in weather reports.

Spelling and Language

A. Trouble Spots

The study words below are missing letters that often cause spelling problems. Think about the letter or letters that fit in the blanks. Then write each word correctly on the lines. You will write some words more than once.

Example: ser__ous = serious

1. pen _ trate _____
2. twel _ _ _ _____
3. asp _ _ in _____
4. cho _ _ late _____
5. fol _ _ ge _____
6. ten _ _ tive _____
7. _ _ _ tatic _____
8. rest _ _ _ ant _____
8. min _ _ ture _____
10. light _ ing _____

11. temp _ _ _ ture _____
12. sep _ rate _____
13. misch _ _ vous _____
14. choco _ _ _ _ _____
15. restau _ _ _ _ _____
16. temper _ _ _ _ _ _____
17. mischiev _ _ _ _____
18. separ _ _ _ _____
19. ath _ _ tics _____
20. veg _ table _____

B. Subject of a Sentence

The subject of a sentence is the noun or noun phrase that tells what or whom the sentence is about. Circle the noun in the subject in each sentence below. Then write it on the line.

Example: The (team) played well.

21. The foliage turned red in the autumn.
22. Lightning flashed in the sky.
23. The high temperature made us perspire.
24. This chocolate tastes delicious.
25. Our restaurant is closed today.

21. _____
22. _____
23. _____
24. _____
25. _____

> **Did You Know?**
> When a word is hard to spell, try making up a memory aid for yourself. For example, to remember that *athletics* has no vowel between *th* and *l*, you can think of the sentence "I'm always breathless after *athletics.*"

Study Words

vegetable
lightning
miniature
athletics
restaurant
ecstatic
tentative
aspirin
chocolate
penetrate
foliage
temperature
separate
twelfth
mischievous

Build Vocabulary

Complete each sentence with a study word.

1. Take two _____ tablets for your fever.
2. You need a thermometer to take Ed's _____ .
3. We added carrots and beans to the _____ soup.
4. The storm brought thunder and _____ .
5. Even the brightest light couldn't _____ the heavy fog.
6. In autumn, the _____ in New England is colorful.
7. The eleventh day is followed by the _____ day.
8. My favorite dessert is _____ pudding.
9. Soccer is part of our school _____ program.
10. Sue was _____ because she won first prize.
11. We ate at a fast-food _____ .
12. I always have to _____ the laundry.
13. We played _____ golf at the carnival.
14. The _____ puppy made us all laugh.
15. We made _____ plans to play baseball if it doesn't rain.

1. _____
2. _____
3. _____
4. _____
5. _____
6. _____
7. _____
8. _____
9. _____
10. _____
11. _____
12. _____
13. _____
14. _____
15. _____

Real-Life Spelling Reading an E-mail Message

E-mail, or electronic mail, is an easy way to communicate on the computer. You can use it to keep in touch with friends and relatives. Read the e-mail message that Diana wrote to her cousin Karen about her summer job. Find six study words and write them on the lines.

16. _____
17. _____
18. _____
19. _____
20. _____
21. _____

FROM: Diana <Diana@abc.com>   TO: Karen @abc.com
DATE: Fri, July 9, 1999 10:16:53 EST
SUBJECT: My Summer Job

Hi Karen,
I just got a summer job! I work as a camp counselor. I was a little tentative about taking the job because I had never worked with children before. Now I'm ecstatic. The kids are great, and the work is fun. We do all kinds of athletics, crafts, and nature activities. Even when the temperature soars into the 90s, we have a good time. Of course, a chocolate ice cream cone helps on those days! Come visit in the fall to see the beautiful foliage.
Diana

Spelling Review

Read each clue below. Then unscramble each set of letters to form study words. Write them on the lines.

	Clue	Scrambled Word	
1.	small copy or model	iaumertin	1. _____
2.	teasing	ucishosemvi	2. _____
3.	after eleventh	whfttle	3. _____
4.	set apart	apastree	4. _____
5.	leaves	aifogle	5. _____
6.	break through	teentreap	6. _____
7.	flavoring from cacao seeds	thoolecac	7. _____
8.	unsure	ivanttete	8. _____
9.	thrilled	cictaste	9. _____
10.	place to eat	suttanarre	10. _____
11.	sports	cashelitt	11. _____
12.	electrical discharge	thigglnin	12. _____
13.	food from plants	glbetevea	13. _____
14.	pain reliever	snipair	14. _____
15.	hotness or coldness	pumeeatterr	15. _____

Spelling and Writing

Write an e-mail message that you might send to a friend or relative. Choose a topic of special interest to you. Organize your ideas on the lines below. Then on another sheet of paper, write your e-mail message. Use as many study words and additional study words as you can.

_____

_____

_____

_____

Spelling Dictionary

How to Use a Dictionary Entry

A dictionary entry tells many things about a word. It can be used to learn about a word's spelling, pronunciation, syllables, part of speech, and meaning. Study the following sample to learn about each part of an entry. All of your study words are entries in this Spelling Dictionary.

Entry Word

The entry words in a dictionary are listed in alphabetical order. Each entry word is shown in dark type to make it easier to find. Each entry word is divided into syllables.

Pronunciation

This is the phonetic spelling of the entry word. It shows how the word is pronounced. The Pronunciation Key on page 107 will help you determine the sound that each symbol stands for. Notice that some words have two accent marks. The primary accent, shown by the longer mark, has more stress.

> **ex·tra·ter·res·tri·al**
> (ek´ strə tə res´ trē əl)
> 1. *adjective* from beyond
> Earth's limits 2. *noun*
> a being from outer space
> p. 42

Part of Speech

The part of speech tells how the entry word can be used in a sentence. Some words can be used in more than one way. When this happens, you will find more than one part of speech in the entry.

Page Number

The page number tells the page on which the entry word first appears in this spelling book.

Definition

The definition tells the meaning of the entry word. If the word has more than one meaning, each definition is numbered. This entry word has two different meanings.

Pronunciation Key

Each letter or symbol in a pronunciation key is followed by one or more key words. The underlined part of a key word tells you how to say the sound of the letter or symbol. Letters of the alphabet stand for most consonant sounds. Because vowels have more than one sound, special marks and letter combinations are used to stand for these sounds.

Learning to use a pronunciation key takes practice. To make it easier, part of this key is also shown on each right-hand page in the Spelling Dictionary.

Symbol	Key Words	Symbol	Key Words
a	asp, fat, parrot	d	dip, beadle, had, dodder
ā	ape, date, play, break, fail	f	fall, after, off, phone
ä	ah, car, father, cot	g	get, haggle, dog
e	elf, ten, berry	h	he, ahead, hotel
ē	even, meet, money, flea	j	joy, agile, badge
i	is, hit, mirror	k	kill, tackle, bake, coat, quick
ī	ice, bite, high, sky	l	let, yellow, ball
ō	open, tone, go, boat	m	met, camel, trim, summer
ô	all, horn, law, oar	n	not, flannel, ton
ႁ	look, pull, moor, wolf	p	put, apple, tap
͞o͞o	ooze, tool, crew, rule	r	red, port, dear, purr
yo͞o	use, cute, few	s	sell, castle, pass, nice
yႁ	cure, globule	t	top, cattle, hat
oi	oil, point, toy	v	vat, hovel, have
ou	out, crowd, plow	w	will, always, swear, quick
u	up, cut, color, flood	y	yet, onion, yard
ur	urn, fur, deter, irk	z	zebra, dazzle, haze, rise
ə	a in ago	ch	chin, catcher, arch, nature
ə	e in agent	sh	she, cushion, dash, machine
ə	i in sanity	th	thin, nothing, truth
ə	o in comply	*th*	then, father, lathe
ə	u in focus	zh	azure, leisure, beige
ər	perhaps, murder	ng	ring, anger, drink
b	bed, fable, dub, ebb		

ac•com•plish (ə käm´ plish) *verb* to do something successfully p. 26

ac•cu•mu•late (ə kyōōm´ yōō lāt´) *verb* to gather or collect p. 26

a•chieve (ə chēv´) *verb* to succeed in doing; to gain by work p. 2

ad•just (ə just´) *verb* to fix, correct, or regulate p. 26

ad•just•ment (ə just´ mənt) *noun* a small alteration or repair p. 46

ad•mis•sion (ad mish´ ən) *noun* 1. a confession or disclosure 2. an entrance fee p. 26

al•li•ance (ə lī´ əns) *noun* a close association; a friendship p. 26

al•ly 1. (al´ ī) *noun* person or country who is a friend 2. (ə lī´) *verb* to join together for a common purpose p. 6

al•ti•tude (al´ tə tōōd´) *noun* the height above sea level p. 70

am•bi•tious (am bish´ əs) *adjective* full of desire for fame or power p. 82

an•a•gram (an´ ə gram´) *noun* a word whose letters can be arranged to spell another word p. 86

an•cient (ān´ chənt) *adjective* 1. of long ago 2. very old p. 18

a•piece (ə pēs´) *adverb* for each person p. 2

ap•pli•ance (ə plī´ əns) *noun* a household machine or tool p. 26

ap•pre•ci•a•tion (ə prē´ shē ā´ shən) *noun* a grateful recognition of help p. 26

ap•prove (ə prōōv´) *verb* to have a good opinion of p. 26

ar•gu•ment (är´ gyōō mənt) *noun* a disagreement or dispute p. 46

ar•ti•fi•cial (ärt´ ə fish´ əl) *adjective* not natural, fake p. 18

as•pi•rin (as´ pə rin´) *noun* a medicine used to relieve fever and pain p. 102

as•sem•ble (ə sem´ bəl) *verb* 1. to gather or meet 2. to put together p. 26

as•sign (ə sīn´) *verb* to give out as a task p. 26

as•sign•ment (ə sīn´ mənt) *noun* a task given out p. 90

as•sist (ə sist´) *verb* to help p. 26

as•sist•ant (ə sis´ tənt) 1. *noun* someone who helps 2. *adjective* assisting; helping p. 98.

as•sort•ment (ə sôrt´ mənt) *noun* a variety of items p. 46

ath•let•ics (ath let´ iks) *noun* sports or games p. 102

at•las (at´ ləs) *noun* from *Atlas*, a Greek mythological character; a reference book of maps p. 94

at•tach•ment (ə tach´ mənt) *noun* a friendship or devotion p. 26

at•tempt (ə tempt´) 1. *verb* to try 2. *noun* a try p. 26

at•tend•ance (ə tend´ əns) *noun* everyone present at an event p. 26

at•ti•tude (at´ ə tōōd´) *noun* a way of behaving, showing feelings p. 70

au•to•graph (ôt´ ə graf´) 1. *noun* a person's signature 2. *verb* to sign your own name on something p. 86

band•age (ban´ dij) *noun* a strip of cloth used to cover an injury p. 70

ban•dan•na (ban dan´ ə) *noun* Hindi; a large square of colored cotton p. 58

ban•quet (bang´ kwət) 1. *noun* French; a formal feast 2. *adjective* having to do with a large feast p. 58

be•fore•hand (bē fôr´ hand´) *adverb* ahead of time; in advance p. 50

bib•li•og•ra•phy (bib´ lē äg´ rə fē) *noun* a list of books used by an author in writing a given work p. 86

bi•ceps (bī´ seps´) *noun* a large muscle in the upper arm p. 66

bi•cy•cle (bī´ sik´ əl) *noun* a vehicle with two wheels, handlebars, pedals, and a seat p. 74

bi•lin•gual (bī ling´ gwəl) *adjective* using or able to speak two languages p. 66

bi•na•ry (bī´ nə rē) *adjective* of a base-two number system in which each number is expressed using only two digits, 0 and 1 p. 66

bin•oc•u•lars (bī näk´ yə lərz) *noun, plural* a viewing device for both eyes that makes distant objects look larger and closer p. 66

bi•og•ra•phy (bī äg´ rə fē) *noun* a nonfiction book about someone's life, written by another person p. 86

blue•print (blōō´ print´) *noun* a plan or diagram for building something, printed in white lines on a blue background p. 14

bo•lo•gna (bə lō´ nē) *noun* from *Bologna*, Italy; a large smoked sausage often sliced and used for sandwiches p. 94

bo•nan•za (bə nan´ zə) *noun* Spanish; 1. a rich gold strike 2. any sudden source of wealth p. 58

Braille (brāl) *noun* from Louis *Braille*, its inventor; a system of writing for the blind that uses raised dots p. 94

brief•ly (brēf´ lē) *adverb* 1. for a short time 2. in very few words p. 2

broc•co•li (bräk´ ə lē) *noun* Italian; a green vegetable with groups of buds growing from a stalk p. 58

a	fat	ᴏᴏ	look	*th*	then
ā	ape	ōō	ooze	zh	azure
ä	father	yōō	use	ng	ring
e	ten	yᴏᴏ	cure	ə	a in ago
ē	even	oi	oil	ə	e in agent
i	hit	ou	out	ə	i in sanity
ī	bite	u	up	ə	o in comply
ō	open	ʉr	fur	ə	u focus
ô	horn	th	thin	ər	perhaps

broom·stick (broom´ stik´) *noun* handle to which a bundle of fibers is fastened to make a broom p. 14

broth·ers-in-law (bru*th*´ ərz in lô´) *noun, plural* 1. the brothers of someone's wife or husband 2. the husbands of someone's sisters p. 30

bruised (broozd) *adjective* injured and discolored p. 14

by·stand·ers (bī´ stand´ ərz) *noun, plural* people not participating in an event, but standing near p. 30

car·toon·ist (kär toon´ ist) *noun* an artist who draws humorous pictures of people and things p. 14

cash·mere (kash´ mir´) *noun* from *Kashmir*, a region in northern India; a soft, combed wool from goats p. 94

cham·pi·on·ship (cham´ pē ən ship´) *noun* the first place in a competition; the highest honor p. 46

choc·o·late (chôk´ ə lət) 1. *noun* a food made from ground and roasted cacao seeds 2. *adjective* made or flavored with chocolate p. 102

clause (klôz) *noun* a group of words with a subject and a verb p. 78

claws (klôz) *noun, plural* curved nails on the foot of an animal p. 78

clue·less (kloo´ lis) *adjective* without a clue; baffled p. 14

con·ceit·ed (kən sēt´ id) *adjective* vain; having too high an opinion of yourself p. 2

con·cise (kən sīs´) *adjective* short and to the point p. 62

con·duc·tor (kən dukt´ ər) *noun* 1. a person in charge of passengers on a train or streetcar 2. a person who leads a band or orchestra p. 90

con·ges·tion (kən jes´ chən) *noun* the condition of being clogged up or overcrowded p. 62

con·scious (kän´ shəs) *adjective* awake; able to feel and think p. 82

con·sist (kən sist´) *verb* to be made up of p. 98

con·sis·tent (kən sis´ tənt) *adjective* always doing things the same way p. 98

con·ven·ience (kən vēn´ yəns) *noun* ease and comfort p. 2

could·'ve (kood´ əv) *contraction* could have p. 22

crafts·man·ship (krafts´ mən ship´) *noun* the skill of an artisan p. 46

cruis·er (krooz´ ər) *noun* 1. a car that travels around an area 2. a fast warship p. 14

cup·fuls (kup´ foolz´) *noun, plural* the amounts a cup will hold p. 30

cy·cle (sī´ kəl) *noun* 1. a period in which a set of events is completed 2. a bicycle or motorcycle p. 74

cy•clist (sīk´ list) *noun* a rider of a bicycle or motorcycle p. 74

cy•clone (sī´ klōn´) *noun* a powerful storm in which strong winds revolve around a center of low pressure p. 74

da•ta (dāt´ ə) *noun, plural* facts and figures p. 30

de•ceive (dē sēv´) *verb* to make someone believe what is not true; mislead p. 2

de•ci•sive (dē sī´ siv) *adjective* 1. settling an argument or contest 2. conclusive p. 62

de•crease (dē krēs´) *verb* to diminish; to become less p. 34

de•duce (dē do͞os´) *verb* figure out from evidence by reasoning p. 90

de•fend (dē fend´) *verb* to guard or protect p. 34

de•mol•ished (di mäl´ ishd) *verb* wrecked or destroyed p. 34

de•par•ture (dē pär´ chər) *noun* a starting on a trip; a leavetaking p. 34

de•prive (dē prīv´) *verb* 1. to take away from 2. to prevent someone from having p. 34

des•ig•nat•ed (dez´ ig nāt´ id) 1. *adjective* named or appointed 2. *verb* pointed out or indicated p. 90

de•signed (di zīnd´) *verb* planned and drew p. 90

de•sir•a•ble (di zīr´ ə bəl) *adjective* worth having p. 34

de•tach (dē tach´) *verb* to unfasten and separate p. 34

de•tect (dē tekt´) *verb* to discover p. 34

di•a•gram (dī´ ə gram) *noun* a drawing to explain something p. 86

die•sel (dē´ zəl) *noun* a type of oil-burning engine p. 2

di•gest (dī´ jest) 1. *noun* a summary of information (dī jest´) 2. *verb* to change food into a form that the body can absorb p. 62

di•ges•tion (di jes´ chən) *noun* the changing of food into a form that the body can absorb p. 62

dis•cus•sion (di skush´ ən) *noun* a conversation or piece of writing about a topic p. 18

duct (dukt) *noun* a tube or channel that conveys a substance, such as air or water p. 90

a	fat	o͞o	look	*th*	then
ā	ape	o͞o	ooze	zh	azure
ä	father	yo͞o	use	ng	ring
e	ten	yo͞o	cure	ə	a in ago
ē	even	oi	oil	ə	e in agent
i	hit	ou	out	ə	i in sanity
ī	bite	u	up	ə	o in comply
ō	open	ʉr	fur	ə	u focus
ô	horn	th	thin	ər	perhaps

dye (dī) 1. *noun* a substance used to color cloth or hair 2. *verb* to color something using dye p. 6

dye•ing (dī´ ing) *verb* coloring something using dye p. 6

dy•ing (dī´ ing) 1. *adjective* about to die 2. *verb* ceasing to live p. 6

dy•nam•ic (dī nam´ ik) *adjective* 1. energetic and vigorous 2. bold and bright p. 6

dy•na•mite (dī´ nə mīt´) 1. *noun* a powerful explosive 2. *verb* to blow up using dynamite p. 6

dy•nas•ty (dī´ nəs tē) *noun* a succession of rulers in the same family p. 6

ec•stat•ic (ek stat´ ik) *adjective* extremely happy p. 102

e•di•tion (ē dish´ ən) *noun* 1. a particular issue of a newspaper 2. all the copies of a book printed at one time p. 18

ed•u•ca•tion•al (ej´ ōō kā´ shən əl) *adjective* giving knowledge p. 90

ed•u•ca•tor (ej´ ōō kāt´ ər) *noun* a teacher p. 90

em•ploy•ment (em ploi´ mənt) *noun* work or occupation p. 46

en•cy•clo•pe•di•a (en sī´ klō pē´ dē ə) *noun* a book or a set of books with alphabetically arranged articles on many subjects p. 74

en•gage•ment (en gāj´ mənt) *noun* 1. a commitment 2. a promise to marry p. 46

ex•tra•cur•ric•u•lar (eks´ trə kə rik´ yōō lər) *adjective* outside of the regular school requirements p. 42

ex•tra•or•di•nar•y (ek strôrd´ ən er´ ē) *adjective* far beyond the ordinary p. 42

ex•tra•ter•res•tri•al (ek´ strə tə res´ trē əl) 1. *adjective* from beyond Earth's limits 2. *noun* a being from outer space p. 42

ex•trav•a•gant (ek strav´ ə gənt) *adjective* costing or spending far too much p. 42

eye•wit•ness (ī´ wit´ nis) *noun* someone who sees or saw something happen p. 50

fa•tigue (fə tēg´) *noun* French; weariness; exhaustion p. 58

fe•ro•cious (fə rō´ shəs) *adjective* fierce and savage p. 82

fire es•cape (fīr´ e skāp´) *noun* an outside stairway for use in escaping from a burning building p. 50

flew (flōō) *verb* 1. traveled through the air 2. made to fly p. 78

flu (flōō) *noun* short for influenza; an illness caused by a virus p. 78

flue (flōō) *noun* a shaft for the passage of smoke or hot air as in a chimney p. 78

fo•li•age (fō´ lē ij´) *noun* leaves, as of plants or trees p. 102

for•eign•er (fôr´ in ər) *noun* a person from another country p. 2

frac•tion (frak´ shən) *noun* a quantity expressed by a numerator and a denominator; a part of a whole p. 62

frac•tured (frak´ chərd) *adjective* broken p. 62

frag•ile (fraj´ əl) *adjective* easily broken p. 62

frag•ment (frag´ mənt) *noun* a small piece of something p. 62

frank•fur•ter (frangk´ fʉrt´ ər) *noun* from *Frankfurt,* Germany; a long sausage eaten on a bun p. 94

gal•va•nize (gal´ və nīz´) *verb* from Luigi *Galvani;* to plate metal with zinc by using electricity p. 94

gen•er•ous (jen´ ər əs) *adjective* 1. unselfish 2. large, abundant p. 82

ge•og•ra•phy (jē äg´ rə fē) *noun* the science that deals with the earth's surface p. 86

ges•tures (jes´ chərz) *noun, plural* hand or body movements p. 62

gi•raffes (jə rafs´) *noun, plural* large African plant-eating animals with long necks and legs p. 30

gla•cier (glā´ shər) *noun* a large, slow-moving mass of ice p. 18

glam•or•ous (glam´ ər əs) *adjective* charming; beautiful p. 82

gon•do•la (gän´ dō lə) *noun* Italian; a slender, small boat used on Venice's canals p. 58

gram•mar (gram´ ər) *noun* a system of rules for writing and speaking in a language p. 86

gram•mat•i•cal (grə mat´ i kəl) *adjective* following the rules for speaking and writing p. 86

graph•ic (graf´ ik) *adjective* in realistic and vivid detail p. 86

grat•i•tude (grat´ i tōōd) *noun* thankful appreciation p. 70

ham•burg•er (ham´ bʉrg´ ər) *noun* from *Hamburg,* Germany; a cooked patty of ground beef, often served on a bun p. 94

han•dle•bars (han´ dəl bärz´) *noun, plural* bars with handles used for steering bicycles p. 50

han•gar (hang´ ər) *noun* a shelter for airplanes p. 78

a	fat	o͝o	look	*th*	then
ā	ape	o͞o	ooze	zh	azure
ä	father	yo͞o	use	ng	ring
e	ten	yo͝o	cure	ə	a in ago
ē	even	oi	oil	ə	e in agent
i	hit	ou	out	ə	i in sanity
ī	bite	u	up	ə	o in comply
ō	open	ʉr	fur	ə	u focus
ô	horn	th	thin	ər	perhaps

han•ger (hang´ ər) *noun* a light frame to hang clothes on p. 78

hers (hʉrz) *pronoun* that or those belonging to her p. 22

hol•o•gram (häl´ ə gram´) *noun* a three-dimensional, laser-made picture of an entire object p. 86

home•sick (hōm´ sik) *adjective* unhappy from being away from home p. 50

hu•mid•i•ty (hyо̅о̅ mid´ ə tē) *noun* the moisture in the air p. 70

hy•drant (hī´ drənt) *noun* a large pipe attached to a water main with a valve for fastening hoses p. 6

i•den•ti•ty (ī den´ tə tē) *noun* the fact of being a particular person or thing p. 70

il•le•gal (il lē´ gəl) *adjective* against the law p. 38

il•log•i•cal (il läj´ i kəl) *adjective* not reasonable; making no sense p. 38

il•lu•sion (i lо̅о̅´ zhən) *noun* a deception; a false impression p. 38

il•lus•trate (il´ əs trāt´) *verb* to furnish a book with pictures p. 38

im•ma•ture (im´ mə tоor´; im´ mə chоor´) *adjective* not completely grown p. 38

im•mi•grate (im´ ə grāt´) *verb* to come to a new country to live p. 38

im•po•lite (im´ pə līt´) *adjective* not having good manners p. 38

im•pris•on (im´ priz´ ən) *verb* to put in jail p. 38

im•prop•er (im präp´ ər) *adjective* not appropriate p. 38

in•ci•sion (in sizh´ ən) *noun* a cut made by a surgeon p. 62

in•ci•sors (in sīz´ ərz) *noun, plural* the front teeth used for cutting p. 62

in•com•plete (in´ kəm plēt´) *adjective* partial; unfinished p. 10

in•con•sis•tent (in´ kən sis´ tənt) *adjective* not always behaving the same p. 98

in•con•ven•ient (in´ kən vēn´ yənt) *adjective* not easy p. 10

in•cor•rect (in´ kə rekt´) *adjective* wrong or mistaken p. 10

in•de•struct•i•ble (in´ di struk´ tə bəl) *adjective* that cannot be destroyed p. 10

in•ex•pen•sive (in´ ek spen´ siv) *adjective* not costly p. 38

in•fec•tion (in fek´ shən) *noun* a disease caused by bacteria or viruses in the body p. 38

in•fi•nite (in´ fə nit) *adjective* 1. limitless, endless 2. not countable p. 10

114 Spelling Dictionary

in•her•it (in her´ it) *verb* to receive the property of someone who has died p. 38

in•i•tial (i nish´ əl) 1. *noun* the letter that begins a name 2. *adjective* first p. 18

in•jus•tice (in jus´ tis) *noun* an unjust or unfair act; a wrong p. 10

in•no•va•tion (in´ ə vā´ shən) *noun* a new device or way of doing something p. 54

in•sist (in sist´) *verb* to demand firmly and repeatedly p. 98

in•sist•ent (in sis´ tənt) *adjective* insisting or demanding p. 98

in•sure (in shoor´) *verb* to protect against loss p. 18

in•tro•duc•to•ry (in´ trə duk´ tə rē) *adjective* leading up to the main action or event p. 90

ir•reg•u•lar (ir reg´ yoo lər) 1. *noun* an imperfect factory product sold at a bargain price 2. *adjective* bumpy or uneven p. 38

ir•re•sis•ti•ble (ir´ ri zis´ tə bəl) *adjective* too tempting to be resisted or refused p. 98

ir•re•spon•si•ble (ir´ ri spän´ sə bəl) *adjective* not trustworthy p. 38

ir•ri•gate (ir´ ə gāt) *verb* to bring in water for crops p. 38

it's (its) *contraction* it is or it has p. 22

its (its) *pronoun* belonging to it p. 22

jun•ior (jōōn´ yər) 1. *adjective* the younger 2. *noun* a student in the next-to-last year of high school or college p. 14

kin•der•gar•ten (kin´ dər gärt´ ən) *noun* German; a school or class for very young children p. 58

know-how (nō´ hou) *noun* ability; skill p. 50

ko•sher (kō´ shər) *adjective* Hebrew; clean or fit to eat according to Jewish dietary laws p. 58

lat•i•tude (lat´ ə tōōd) *noun* distance north or south of the equator p. 70

lead•er•ship (lēd´ ər ship´) *noun* 1. guidance 2. the ability to take charge and guide others p. 46

left•o•vers (left´ ō´ vərz) *noun, plural* unused things that remain, such as uneaten food p. 30

a	fat	**ʘʘ**	look	**th**	then
ā	ape	**ōō**	ooze	**zh**	azure
ä	father	**yʘʘ**	use	**ng**	ring
e	ten	**yʘʘ**	cure	**ə**	a in ago
ē	even	**oi**	oil	**ə**	e in agent
i	hit	**ou**	out	**ə**	i in sanity
ī	bite	**u**	up	**ə**	o in comply
ō	open	**ʉr**	fur	**ə**	u focus
ô	horn	**th**	thin	**ər**	perhaps

le•o•tard (lē′ ə tärd′) *noun* from Jules *Léotard;* a tight-fitting dance garment p. 94

let's (lets) *contraction* let us p. 22

light•ning (līt′ ning) *noun* a flash of light in the sky caused by a discharge of electricity p. 102

lon•gi•tude (län′ jə tōōd′) *noun* distance east or west of the prime meridian, a line running through Greenwich, England p. 70

ma•jor•i•ty (mə jôr′ ə tē) *noun* the greater number or part; more than half of the total p. 70

man•age•ment (man′ ij mənt) *noun* the persons supervising a business p. 46

ma•neu•ver (mə nōō′ vər; mə nyōō′ vər) *verb* to perform a skilled movement p. 14

ma•roon (mə rōōn′) 1. *adjective* dark brownish red 2. *verb* to leave someone in a lonely place p. 14

mas•ter•piece (mas′ tər pēs′) *noun* the greatest work done by a person or group p. 50

me•di•a (mē′ dē ə) *noun, plural* the various means of mass communication p. 30

mem•ber•ship (mem′ bər ship′) *noun* all the people in a club or group p. 46

me•ter (mēt′ ər) *noun* the basic metric unit of measurement p. 74

me•ter•stick (mēt′ ər stik′) *noun* a graduated measuring stick one meter in length p. 74

met•ric (me′ trik) *adjective* related to a system of weights and measures based on tens p. 74

met•ro•nome (me′ trə nōm′) *noun* an instrument that makes clicking sounds at an even rate, used when practicing a musical instrument p. 74

mil•li•me•ter (mil′ i mēt′ ər) *noun* a thousandth of a meter p. 74

min•i•a•ture (min′ ē ə chər) *adjective* very small p. 102

mi•nor•i•ty (mī nôr′ ə tē) *noun* the lesser number or part; less than half of the total p. 70

mi•rac•u•lous (mi rak′ yōō ləs) *adjective* having no rational explanation; remarkable p. 82

mis•chie•vous (mis′ chə vəs) *adjective* teasing or prankish p. 102

mis•for•tune (mis fôr′ chən) *noun* trouble; unluckiness p. 34

mis•judge (mis juj′) *verb* to judge unfairly or wrongly p. 34

mis•lead (mis lēd′) *verb* to deceive p. 34

mis•no•mer (mis nō′ mər) *noun* an incorrect name for a thing p. 54

mis•sion (mish′ ən) *noun* an assignment a person is sent out to do p. 18

mis•step (mi step´) *noun* 1. a stumble 2. an error or mistake p. 34

mis•tak•en (mi stāk´ ən) *adjective* wrong p. 34

mis•trust (mis trust´) *verb* to regard with suspicion p. 34

mis•un•der•stood (mis´ un dər stood´) *verb* failed to understand correctly p. 34

mon•arch (män´ ərk) *noun* 1. a hereditary ruler 2. a large orange and black butterfly p. 66

mon•o•gram (män´ ə gram´) *noun* the initials of someone's name, made into a design p. 66

mon•o•plane (män´ ō plān´) *noun* an airplane with one pair of wings p. 66

mo•nop•o•ly (mə näp´ ə lē) *noun* the control of a product or service by one company in a particular market p. 66

mo•not•o•nous (mə nät´ ə nəs) *adjective* boring because of lack of variety p. 66

mon•soon (män soon´) *noun* Arabic; 1. the seasonal wind in the Indian Ocean and Southern Asia 2. the rainy season in these places, from June to September p. 58

morn•ing (môrn´ ing) *noun* the first part of a day; before noon p. 78

mo•tor•cy•cle (mōt´ ər sī´ kəl) *noun* a two-wheeled vehicle powered by an engine p. 74

mourn•ing (môrn´ ing) 1. *noun* a period during which a person feels grief after a loss 2. *verb* feeling sorrow after a loss p. 78

nerv•ous (nʉr´ vəs) *adjective* tense; restless; anxious p. 82

neu•tral (noo´ trəl; nyoo´ trəl) *adjective* impartial p. 14

nom•i•nal (näm´ ə nəl) *adjective* very small or insignificant p. 54

nom•i•nate (näm´ ə nāt´) *verb* to suggest as a candidate for elected office p. 54

nom•i•na•tion (näm´ ə nā´ shən) *noun* the naming of someone as a candidate for election p. 54

nom•i•nee (näm´ ə nē´) *noun* someone who is named as a candidate for election p. 54

non•ex•ist•ent (nän´ eg zist´ ənt) *adjective* not real; imaginary p. 10

non•fat (nän´ fat´) *adjective* containing no fat p. 10

a	fat	oo	look	*th*	then
ā	ape	ōō	ooze	zh	azure
ä	father	yōō	use	ng	ring
e	ten	yoo	cure	ə	a in ago
ē	even	oi	oil	ə	e in agent
i	hit	ou	out	ə	i in sanity
ī	bite	u	up	ə	o in comply
ō	open	ʉr	fur	ə	u focus
ô	horn	th	thin	ər	perhaps

non•fic•tion (nän´ fik´ shən)
1. *noun* writing that tells a story
about real people or events
2. *adjective* telling a story about
real people or events p. 10

non•prof•it (nän´ präf´ it)
adjective run for a purpose other
than to make money p. 10

non•re•fund•a•ble
(nän´ ri fund´ ə bəl) *adjective*
not reimbursable; cannot be given
back p. 10

non•sched•uled (nän´ ske´ jσold)
adjective not planned to occur at a
certain time p. 10

non•sense (nän´ sens) *noun*
words or actions that are
meaningless or silly p. 10

non•stop (nän´ stäp´) *adjective*
without making any stops p. 10

non•vi•o•lent (nän´ vī´ ə lənt)
adjective not using violence;
peaceful p. 10

noun (noun) *noun* a word that
names a person, place, thing, or
idea p. 54

no•va (nō´ və) *noun* a star that
brightens and then dims p. 54

nov•el (näv´ əl) *noun* a long
fiction book p. 54

nov•el•ette (näv´ əl et´) *noun*
a short novel p. 54

nov•el•ist (näv´ əl ist) *noun*
someone who writes novels p. 54

nov•ice (näv´ is) *noun* a beginner
at a skill p. 54

nui•sance (nōō´ səns; nyōō´ səns)
noun a person or thing that is
annoying p. 14

nu•mer•ous (nōō´ mər əs)
adjective many p. 82

ny•lon (nī´ län) *noun* a strong
synthetic fiber p. 6

ob•vi•ous (äb´ vē əs) *adjective*
easy to see and understand p. 82

od•ys•sey (äd´ i sē) *noun* from
Odysseus, a Greek hero; 1. a long
eventful journey 2. [O-] an ancient
Greek poem about the wanderings
of Odysseus p. 94

on•look•ers (än´ lōōk´ ərz) *noun,*
plural the people watching an
event p. 30

o•ri•ga•mi (ôr´ ə ga´ mē) *noun*
Japanese; the art of folding paper
into animals or flowers p. 58

ours (ourz) *pronoun* that or
those belonging to us p. 22

over•due (ō´ vər dōō´; ō vər
dyōō´) *adjective* past the time due
for arrival or payment p. 14

ox•en (äks´ ən) *noun, plural*
domesticated bulls used as draft
animals p. 30

pan•ic (pan´ ik) *noun* from the
Greek god *Pan;* the emotion of
sudden fear p. 94

par•a•chute (par´ ə sho͞ot´) *noun*
French; an umbrella-like cloth that
slows a person's fall when jumping
out of an airplane p. 58

pa•ren•the•ses (pə ren´ thə sēz)
noun, plural a pair of curved lines,
( ), used to set off an explanatory
part of a sentence p. 30

part•ner•ship (pärt´ nər ship´)
noun 1. a joint effort or alliance
2. a business jointly owned by two
or more people p. 46

pas•sage (pas´ ij) *noun*
1. a portion of a piece of writing or
music 2. a way through which a
person or thing may pass p. 70

pas•teur•ize (pas´ cher īz´) *verb*
from Louis *Pasteur*; to sterilize milk
or other foods by heating p. 94

pa•tience (pā´ shəns) *noun* the
ability to wait calmly p. 78

pa•tients (pā´ shəns) *noun,*
plural people receiving medical
care p. 78

pen•e•trate (pen´ i trāt´) *verb* to
enter into or through p. 102

per•sist (pər sist´) *verb* to
continue firmly in spite of
opposition p. 98

per•sist•ence (pər sist´ əns) *noun*
a continuing in the face of
opposition p. 98

per•sist•ent (pər sist´ ənt)
adjective continuing or
persevering p. 98

pho•tog•ra•phy (fə täg´ rə fē)
noun the making of pictures on a
light-sensitive surface, such as
film p. 86

pic•to•graph (pik´ tō graf´) *noun*
a graph that uses pictures to
represent quantities p. 86

place•ment (plās´ mənt) *noun*
a position; assignment p. 46

pla•teau (pla tō´) *noun* French;
a high, flat area of land p. 58

pol•ish (päl´ ish) 1. *noun* a
substance rubbed on a surface to
make it shiny 2. *verb* to rub until
shiny p. 18

por•tion (pôr´ shən) *noun* a single
serving p. 18

pre•cise•ly (prē sīs´ lē) *adverb*
exactly; carefully p. 62

pres•sure (presh´ ər) 1. *noun* the
act of pushing down on 2. *noun*
stressful demands on a person's
time or strength 3. *verb* to exert
force to get someone to act p. 18

a	fat	o͞o	look	*th*	then
ā	ape	o͞o	ooze	zh	azure
ä	father	yo͞o	use	ng	ring
e	ten	yo͞o	cure	ə	a in ago
ē	even	oi	oil	ə	e in agent
i	hit	ou	out	ə	i in sanity
ī	bite	u	up	ə	o in comply
ō	open	ʉr	fur	ə	u focus
ô	horn	th	thin	ər	perhaps

pre•vi•ous (prē´ vē əs) *adjective* happening at an earlier time p. 82

pro•duc•tive (prō duk´ tiv) *adjective* yielding profits or value p. 90

pro•gram•mer (prō´ gram ər) *noun* a person who writes coded instructions for computers p. 86

pro•noun (prō´ noun) *noun* a word used to take the place of a noun p. 54

pro•te•in (prō´ tēn) *noun* any of a large group of complex organic compounds containing nitrogen that are essential to diet p. 2

rapt (rapt) *adjective* with complete attention p. 78

re•ceiv•er (ri sēv´ ər) *noun* 1. a person who receives 2. device that converts an electrical signal into a useful form; a telephone receiver p. 2

re•cy•cle (rē sī´ kəl) *verb* to use over and over p. 74

re•duce (ri dōōs´) *verb* to make less or lower p. 90

re•fract•ed (ri frak´ təd) *adjective* bent, as a ray of light passing through water p. 62

re•fresh•ment (ri fresh´ mənt) *noun* food or drink or both p. 46

re•lieve (ri lēv´) *verb* to lessen a burden or pain p. 2

re•li•gious (ri lij´ əs) *adjective* devout; pious p. 82

ren•o•vate (ren´ ə vāt) *verb* to modernize or make new again p. 54

re•pro•duce (rē´ prə dōōs´) *verb* to make a copy p. 90

re•sign (ri zīn´) *verb* to give up a position or job p. 90

re•sist (ri zist´) *verb* to withstand, as a temptation p. 98

re•sist•ance (ri zist´ əns) *noun* 1. power to resist 2. the opposition of some force p. 98

re•sist•ant (ri zist´ ənt) *adjective* resisting or opposing p. 98

res•tau•rant (res´ tə ränt´) *noun* a place to buy and eat meals p. 102

re•triev•er (ri trēv´ ər) *noun* a dog trained to bring back animals hunted for sport p. 2

rhine•stone (rīn´ stōn´) *noun* from the *Rhine* River; a glittery, artificial gemstone p. 94

rhyme (rīm) 1. *noun* a poem whose lines have similar ending sounds 2. *verb* to make the same ending sounds as another word p. 6

roofs (rōōfs) *noun, plural* outside top coverings of buildings p. 30

rye (rī) *noun* a grain used to make flour p. 6

sal•sa (säl´ sə) *noun* Spanish; a spicy sauce often used as a dip for tortilla chips p. 58

schol•ar•ship (skäl´ ər ship´) *noun* a gift of money to help a student pay for his or her education p. 46

seized (sēzd) *verb* grabbed or captured p. 2

self-de•fense (self´ dē fens´) *noun* the defense of yourself p. 50

sep•a•rate (sep´ ə rāt) 1. *verb* to break apart or set apart (sep´ ər it) 2. *adjective* set apart from the others; distinct p. 102

series (sir´ ēz) *noun, plural* a sequence of events, games, or numbers p. 30

se•ri•ous (sir´ ē əs) *adjective* 1. very grave or important 2. not joking p. 82

ses•sion (sesh´ ən) *noun* a meeting, appointment, or period of activity p. 18

sheer (shir) *adjective* transparent; very thin p. 18

sher•iffs (sher´ ifs) *noun, plural* the chief law enforcement officers of counties p. 30

ship•wreck (ship´ rek´) *noun* the loss or remains of a ship in a storm p. 50

short•age (shôrt´ ij) *noun* the condition of not having enough of something p. 70

should•'ve (shood´ əv) *contraction* should have p. 22

shut•tle (shut´ əl) *noun* a vehicle that travels back and forth over a short route p. 18

shy•ness (shī´ nəs) *noun* bashfulness; timidity p. 6

side ef•fects (sīd´ e fekts´) *noun, plural* effects that happen in addition to the desired effect p. 50

sign lan•guage (sīn´ lang´ gwij) *noun* a language that uses gestures to communicate p. 50

sig•nif•i•cance (sig nif´ ə kəns) *noun* 1. the meaning 2. the importance p. 90

sig•ni•fy (sig´ nə fī) *verb* 1. to be a sign of 2. to express or indicate p. 90

sim•i•lar•i•ty (sim´ i ler´ ə tē) *noun* a resemblance p. 70

six•teen•year•olds (siks tēn´ yēr ōldz) *noun, plural* people who are sixteen years old p. 30

a	fat	oo	look	*th*	then
ā	ape	ōō	ooze	zh	azure
ä	father	yōō	use	ng	ring
e	ten	yoo	cure		a in ago
ē	even	oi	oil		e in agent
i	hit	ou	out		i in sanity
ī	bite	u	up		o in comply
ō	open	ᵤr	fur		u focus
ô	horn	th	thin	r	perhaps

skied (skēd) *verb* slid downhill on two runners p. 2

spe•cies (spē´ shēz) *noun* 1. kind or type 2. group of related animals or plants p. 30

sta•tion•ar•y (stā´ shə ner´ ē) *adjective* standing still; staying in one place p. 78

sta•tion•er•y (stā´ shə ner´ ē) *noun* writing paper and envelopes p. 78

stop•watch (stäp´ wäch´) *noun* a watch you can start and stop to time events p. 50

sub•sist (səb sist´) *verb* to manage to stay alive p. 98

sug•gest•ed (səg jest´ əd) *verb* brought up as a possibility p. 62

su•per•fi•cial (soo´ pər fish´ əl) *adjective* 1. on the surface 2. concerned with only the obvious; shallow p. 42

su•per•high•way (soo´ pər hī´ wā) *noun* a divided road for high-speed traffic p. 42

su•per•hu•man (soo´ pər hyoo´ mən) *adjective* greater than that of an ordinary human being p. 42

su•per•la•tive (soo pur´ lə tiv) *adjective* better than all the others; excellent p. 42

su•per•mar•ket (soo´ pər mär´ kit) *noun* a large, self-service food store p. 42

su•per•no•va (soo´ pər nō´ və) *noun* a very bright nova, or star that flares intensely and then gradually fades out p. 54

su•per•pow•er (soo´ pər pou´ ər) *noun* one of the mightiest, most influential nations p. 42

su•per•son•ic (soo´ pər sän´ ik) *adjective* of speeds faster than that of sound p. 42

su•per•star (soo´ pər stär) *noun* someone who excels at sports or entertainment p. 42

su•per•sti•tious (soo´ pər sti´ shəs) *adjective* believing that supernatural forces exist and that certain actions will please or anger them p. 82

sure•ly (shoor´ lē) *adverb* certainly; without doubt p. 18

sweatshirt or **sweat shirt** (swet´ shʉrt´) *noun* an absorbent pullover that soaks up sweat p. 50

tan•ge•rine (tan´ jə rēn´) *noun* from *Tangier*, Morocco; a small, loose-skinned orange p. 94

tape-re•cord (tāp´ ri kôrd´) *verb* to record sounds on magnetic tape p. 50

tel•e•gram (tel´ ə gram) *noun* a message sent by telegraph p. 86

tel•e•graph (tel′ ə graf) 1. *noun* a system for sending a message electrically 2. *verb* to send by telegraph p. 86

tem•per•a•ture (tem′ pər ə chər) *noun* the degree of hotness or coldness of a person or thing p. 102

ten•ta•tive (ten′ tə tiv) *adjective* temporary; subject to change p. 102

tes•ti•fy (tes′ tə fī) *verb* to declare, especially under oath in court p. 6

their (ther) *pronoun* belonging to them p. 22

ther•mom•e•ter (thər mäm′ ət ər) *noun* an instrument for measuring temperatures p. 74

they're (ther) *contraction* they are p. 22

to•bog•gan (tə bäg′ ən) *noun* Algonquian; a long sled without runners p. 58

touch•down (tuch′ doun′) *noun* a play in football worth six points that ends with the ball over the opponent's goal line p. 50

town•ship (toun′ ship) *noun* a division of a county that is a unit of local government p. 46

tri•an•gle (trī′ ang əl) *noun* a plane figure with three sides and three angles p. 66

tri•cy•cle (trī′ sik əl) *noun* a child's three-wheeled vehicle with pedals p. 74

tril•lion (tril′ yən) *noun* a thousand billion; 1 followed by 12 zeroes p. 66

tri•o (trē′ ō) *noun* a group of three musicians p. 66

tri•ple (trip′ əl) *adjective* consisting of three parts or three things p. 66

tri•plets (trip′ lits) *noun, plural* three children born at a single birth p. 66

tri•pod (trī′ päd) *noun* a three-legged stand for a camera p. 66

twelfth (twelfth) *adjective* next after the eleventh p. 102

type•writ•er (tīp′ rīt′ ər) *noun* an office machine with a keyboard that prints letters p. 6

ty•rant (tī′ rənt) *noun* a cruel ruler p. 6

ul•tra•mod•ern (ul′ trə mäd′ ərn) *adjective* extremely up-to-date p. 42

a	fat	o͝o	look	*th*	then
ā	ape	o͞o	ooze	zh	azure
ä	father	yo͞o	use	ng	ring
e	ten	yo͝o	cure	ə	a in ago
ē	even	oi	oil	ə	e in agent
i	hit	ou	out	ə	i in sanity
ī	bite	u	up	ə	o in comply
ō	open	ʉr	fur	ə	u focus
ô	horn	th	thin	ər	perhaps

ul•tra•son•ic (ul′ trə sän′ ik) *adjective* above the range of sound that humans can hear p. 42

ul•tra•vi•o•let (ul′ trə vī′ ə lit) *adjective* past the violet end of the visible spectrum of light p. 42

u•nan•i•mous (yo͞o nan′ ə məs) *adjective* in total agreement p. 82

un•as•sist•ed (un′ ə sist′ əd) *adjective* without help p. 98

un•con•scious (un kän′ shəs) *adjective* not aware of one's surroundings; without consciousness p. 82

u•ni•cy•cle (yo͞on′ ə sī′ kəl) *noun* a vehicle with pedals and one wheel p. 74

u•nit (yo͞on′ it) *noun* 1. a person or thing that is part of a larger group, such as an emergency vehicle that is part of a fleet 2. a distinct part with a special purpose, such as a section of a textbook p. 14.

u•ni•verse (yo͞on′ ə vɹrs′) *noun* all of reality, including the Earth, stars, planets, and outer space p. 14

un•true (un tro͞o′) *adjective* false; not correct p. 14

us•age (yo͞o′ sij) *noun* 1. a way of using something 2. the customary way in which words and phrases are used p. 70

veg•e•ta•ble (vej′ ət ə bəl) 1. *noun* part of a plant used as food

2. *adjective* from a plant, not from animal or inorganic material p. 102

volt•age (vōl′ tij) *noun* from Alessandro *Volta;* the electromotive force, expressed in volts p. 94

watt•age (wät′ ij) *noun* from James *Watt;* the amount of electrical power, expressed in watts p. 94

weird (wird) *adjective* strange or mysterious p. 2

we're (wir) *contraction* we are p. 22

what's (hwuts) *contraction* what is, what has, or what does p. 22

would•'ve (wo͝od′ əv) *contraction* would have p. 22

wrapped (rapt) *verb* enfolded in paper or cloth p. 78

wreck•age (rek′ ij) *noun* the remains after a wreck p. 70

your (yo͝or) *pronoun* belonging to you p. 22

you're (yo͝or) *contraction* you are p. 22

yours (yo͝orz) *pronoun* that or those belonging to you p. 22

zuc•chi•ni (zo͞o kē′ nē) *noun* Italian; a variety of summer squash resembling a cucumber p. 58

Spelling and Writing

Correct spelling is an important part of effective writing. Your readers will have an easier time understanding your ideas if your writing is free of errors. Here are some additional ideas to help you become an effective writer.

Using the Writing Process

The writing process is a step-by-step plan for putting your ideas in writing. Follow the steps below.

Prewriting

In the prewriting step, choose your audience and your purpose for writing. After choosing a topic, jot down your ideas. Lists, webs, outlines, charts, and sketches can help you organize your thoughts.

Drafting

In the drafting step, write about the ideas you organized in the prewriting step. This is not the time to worry about mistakes. You can fix them later.

Revising

In the revising step, carefully reread your draft. You may also want to share it with others. Check to make sure you have an interesting beginning and a strong ending. Find and rewrite incomplete sentences. Add details to make your writing more interesting. Check that your words say exactly what you mean. Make any changes that you need.

Proofreading

In the proofreading step, check your revised draft. Look for misspelled words and correct them. Check that capital letters are used correctly. Add or change punctuation. Fix mistakes in grammar.

Publishing

In the publishing step, share your writing with others. You can print out your writing from a computer. You can read it aloud or make a tape. You can also use your writing and pictures to make a poster, a book, or an advertisement.

Taking a Writing Test

Many states now give students a writing test. The work that you do in spelling will help you succeed on this test. Knowing what will be on the test and how the test will be graded can also help you prepare.

What is on the writing test?

One section of the test will include questions with a choice of different answers. This is called a *multiple-choice test*. Here's an example of a multiple-choice question:

Direction: Read the sentence. Mark the circle to indicate the word that is misspelled. Mark circle D if there are no mistakes.

1. Ⓐ Ⓑ Ⓒ Ⓓ   We rode <u>through</u> the <u>valley</u> on <u>donkies</u>.
                           A   B   C

To answer this kind of question, first read the sentence and think about its meaning. Then look at each underlined word in the sentence. Check for errors in spelling and grammar. Look for mistakes in capitalization and punctuation. Check for errors in the way words are used in the sentence. Remember, a word's spelling may depend on how it is used in a sentence.

Another section of the test will ask you to write an essay. You may be given a topic to write about. In your essay, correct spelling is important. Proofread your essay, and correct errors in spelling, grammar, capitalization, and punctuation.

What can I do to get a good grade?

Preparation and practice will help you to get a good grade.

- Prepare by studying your spelling words each week.
- Practice writing as much and as often as you can. The more you write, the better you will become at writing.
- Learn to recognize a word that is misspelled. Try different spellings until the word looks right. Then check your guess.
- To correct a misspelled word, say the word. Then try to see the correct spelling in your mind. Look for patterns. Think about spelling rules. Look at the shape of the word. Pay attention to the hard part or parts of the word.
- Keep a list of words that you have trouble spelling. Practice spelling these words.
- Learn how much time you can give to each part of the test.
- Have confidence in yourself. You have good ideas.